C000199238

The Pineapple King of Jarrow

& Other Stories

Alex Ferguson

from the
award-winning
BBC Radio 4 Series,
My Uncle Freddie

This Edition first published 2004 by:
IRON Press
5 Marden Tce
Cullercoats
North Shields
NE30 4PD.
Tel/Fax 0191-2531901
e-mail: seaboy@freenetname.co.uk
web site: www.ironpress.co.uk

Typeset in Garamond 10 pt

Printed by Field Print, Boldon Colliery, Tyne and Wear

The *Uncle Freddie* stories ran in six series on BBC Radio 4
between 1994 and 2000
The stage version toured with NTC Touring in 1995

ISBN 0 906228 50 6

IRON Press books are distributed by Central Books
IRON Press is represented by Inpress Ltd
Telephone +44 (0) 1234 330023
email john@inpressbooks.co.uk
web www.inpressbooks.co.uk

Foreword

Even now I can see the bright mornings when my Uncle Freddie and I were out in the back lane of Hurworth Place weaving from wall to wall the pattern of washing lines that dominated my childhood. Other children remember landscapes of snowy delight. Cornish cliff tops where the gulls ride the wind. Or donkeys grazing in golden fields of buttercups.

I remember wet sheets and the boiling copper, the rub-a-dub-dub of the poss-stick, aching arms and churning mangles, the sight and smell of yellow soap and washboards, and finally the hoisting of laundry on clothes props like a vast array of flags filling the lane to signal another painful victory in the never-ending battle with other folks' dirty washing.

When a bright breeze blew on washdays the back lanes of Jarrow were a majestic sight. It was as if the whole scrubby town had set sail, full sail, like China clippers, to quit the tired, sooty Tyne and fly before the wind to faraway Cathay.

|Alex Ferguson|

Alex Ferguson runs the notorious Bold As Brass Theatre Company on South Tyneside. He cherishes a C. P. Taylor Bursary, a Play of the Month Award (West End), shared a Guinness National Award for Pub Theatre, won a Writers' Guild Award for Comedy, a Sony Nomination for Creative Radio Writing and a Royal Television Society nomination for the film Lads! His most treasured accolade is the Tiny Tots Order of Merit for keeping the colour inside the lines.

Contents

— To my mother and father —

The Pineapple King of Jarrow

In the nineteen thirties when I was a skinny bairn, more bones and gristle than a ninepenny rabbit, I lived with Our Mam and Our Dad and my sisters, Nancy and Peggy and Granny and Grandad Fergie at 1 Hurworth Place, Jarrow on Tyne. We lived upstairs with the Best Room, a bedroom, kitchen and a cupboard on the landing. We all fitted in cosily because Our Nancy and then Our Peggy were away in service at Panhacklety House, Granny and Grandad slept in the kitchen and Our Dad worked night shifts on one leg at the Co-op Bakery. He never came home to a cold bed. I slept like a prince in the Best Room. While downstairs in number two, with only the two rooms, lived my beloved Uncle Freddie, an unemployed shipwright and my Auntie Bella, an earthbound angel, who was also my mother's sister. The pair of them, Mary and Bella, worked together in the washhouse in our yard doing the laundry for lucky women whose husbands were able to afford them the luxury of not possing, scrubbing, ironing and mending. For all their labour these women paid Our Mam and Auntie Bella a pittance. When Palmer's shipyard closed in 1933 and the town died from a massive haemorrhage of hope and pride no one has ever staunched, Freddie had too much time on his hands and so we got the job of looking after one another. I don't remember a time when he didn't hold my hand and my heart.

It was our habit, Uncle Freddie and me, when our chores at the poss tub or the washing lines were done, to recline, Freddie on a kitchen chair and me on my beer crate in sunny state out the front of Hurworth Place. I would wear my tin hat from the War and Uncle Freddie his cap upon his nose while he would tell me true stories, stories so true that even if you held them up against the light you couldn't see through them.

"My keen eyes had saved the Titanic, "exclaimed Uncle Freddie, his empty pipe punctuating the story with gentle plops, "the CALIFORNIAN sheered off and everybody breathed again. Then the Captain sent up the bows for the lookout to come aft, and so, very reluctantly, mind you, old son, 'cause we're in iceberg country I leave me post and walk back to the bridge."

Plop, plop, went the pipe. Flutter, flutter, went my heart. That's my Uncle Freddie, a magical storyteller. The man who brought sunshine through Jarrow's soot into my childhood. He has me, Lecky Fergie, his favourite nephew, as mesmerised as any welsh rarebit with the story of how he saved the TITANIC.

"When I got to the bridge," said Uncle Freddie, settling for a long haul on his sunwarmed throne, "They were all there. The officers, that is. Brave men who'd proved themselves. Chief Officer Wilde, Mr. Murdoch, First Officer, Mr. Lightoller, Second Officer. There was a middy there I didn't know, little more than a bairn, white as a sheet. He burst out with, 'Well done, Dean, without you we'd've all been gonners that time!'"

Plop, plop! Flutter, flutter of pride. Most of the time we were nearly gonners. At that time in Jarrow we sailed on the edge of a whirlpool that threatened to overwhelm us at any moment and suck us down into the depths of destitution where we would all surely drown. Even the little cabin boy, Lecky. Palmers, the great shipyard, universal employer of all Jarrow was shut forever and our sure world was shattered as a broken chamberpot.
"The Old Man was Captain Edward J. Smith. One of the best. Always tried out any new ship for the Line," Uncle Freddie declared.
"But he was glad you were there, Uncle Freddie, wasn't he?" I persisted, "You saved the TITANIC for him."
"Oh, he was glad right enough. In private, of course, I called him Ted and he always called me Freddie. In front of the officers it was more formal as you'd expect. But he depended on me for advice."
"He was lucky you were there."
"I was attached to the TITANIC as a special consultant, old son. Just for the maiden voyage. But I insisted on sharing duties with the crew."

I really wanted to ask how he was attached to the TITANIC. Rope or chain? But he was well-launched on the story, this king of dreamers, in the shabby shirt, neatly turned and patched by Granny Fergie, old shiny trousers with empty pockets, knobby boots shiny as a blackleaded boiler, filling my head with dreams. Thank God he did! Is there a better gift to give a child than an elastic-sided imagination?

"But on this occasion all formality was cast aside and there was a tear in his eye when the Captain stepped forward and said, 'Freddie Dean,' he said and he put a hand on each shoulder. I could smell his dinner I was that close. I said, 'Begging your pardon, Captain, but there's no bow look-out. 'Never mind that for now,' he said, 'Freddie Dean, I cannot thank you enough. Your sharp eyes have saved the TITANIC and when we reach New York I will see to it that you, Freddie Dean'..."

Plop, plop, went the pipe.

"Yes, Uncle Freddie, yes, what was it he would see to it that you?"
"I never found out, old son," said Uncle Freddie and removed his pipe from his mouth as a mark of respect.
"Why not?"
"At that very moment when the Captain was saying, 'When we reach New York I will see to it that you, Freddie Dean' the TITANIC struck an iceberg and started to sink."
"It didn't!"
"It did, old son."
"Tell me it didn't!"
"How can I tell you that? It did sink. It was supposed to be unsinkable, but it still went to the bottom."
"How did it come to hit the iceberg?"
"How? There was no look-out on the bow."
"Then it was you sank the Titanic!"
"No! It wasn't my fault. I'd been ordered from my post."
I could hear the concern in his voice and see the anxiety in his face. His story had hit an iceberg and was sinking fast.
I accused him directly.
"You said this story was called How I Saved the TITANIC. Not How I Sank the TITANIC."
"I saved it the first time, old sausage. I couldn't save it every time."
"Then why didn't you get drownded?"

I was near to drowning in a sea of cynicism. Waves of disbelief were swamping my gullibility. I was taking in salt water fast. My bilges were bulging. The bright day had darkened and a cloud as lumpy as an ocean liner had covered the sun.
"Because," he said, uncertainly.
"Because what?"

Plop, plop, said his empty pipe, sucking desperately for inspiration.
"Because what, Uncle Freddie?"
"Because I made a boat," said my Uncle Freddie, triumphantly and settled into his chair a little easier. Plop, plop! Sucks boo to you, old squirt!
"What did you make your boat from?"
"What did I make my boat from?"
"Yes."
"Deck chairs, old sausage. Deck chairs. The place was littered with them. And the canvas, of course, made a very canny little sail," said the magician, pulling out the Flags of All the Nations from his sleeve, releasing snowy doves from his celluloid cuffs and raising his shiny topper to display a white rabbit sitting on his head. Da-daa! Wild applause from the audience.

Uncle Freddie's fragile catamaran of deck chairs and canvas set sail in my head against the lights of the doomed liner, dwarfed by the arctic sky and with one bound of the imagination, one perilous leap, our hero was free, riding along on the crest of a wave, all our eyes on the distant horizon, looking out for passers-by.

The beauty of his stories was that there was always a foundation of edible truth; some morsel of swallowability; some speck of prime pork in his most outrageous sausage; but if you look up the record of that tragic April night in nineteen twelve you'll find no mention of F.W. Dean and his homemade boat. I wonder why not? Modesty, d'y'suppose? I was soon to learn the reason why.

"But you didn't just save yourself, Uncle Freddie, did you? You didn't leave anyone behind, did you?"

He gave me a reproachful glance, but I wanted no one to drown in the arctic sea of confusion. I wanted a world that was safe and sure. Where no one drowned in loneliness. Where for every desperate hand there was the firm grip of a true friend. Where every broken heart was mended with Sure-Fix glue. Where no hungry babby screamed in an empty house and no one stood in cold darkness weeping to find a safe place to sleep.

Yet here we were, all of us, alone in an empty, echoing sea, struggling to keep our noses above water, desperately listening for far-off splashing that might signal other human life. Or the approach of sharks.

"I know you wouldn't leave anyone."

How solemn was the child I am. How lucky to have an uncle like Freddie Dean. He tugged at his pipe, looking at me sidelong, considering, weighing his words.
"I brought away what I could, old son. Yi know I would always do my duty. But the real hero of the night was the little lady who kept us all cheered and cheerful through those dark hours. Can you keep a secret, Lecky? A deathly secret? A cross your heart and swear to die secret?"
I could hardly breathe. My crossing hand trembled in mid-cross. My heart beat like a poss stick. I was surprised he didn't complain of the noise.
"Yes, I can," I whispered, aware that Mrs. Chamberlain's cat was listening intently, "I can, Uncle Freddie. Until the day I die or even longer."
My eyes were glued to his face like a dog to a pound of sausages.

"Not many folk know this," said Uncle Freddie, solemnly, slowly, "But I had the good fortune to rescue the marvellous moppet herself."
"Shirley Temple?" I whispered, "Shirley Temple!"
He nodded in agreement as I spoke the Holy Name, but tapped his nose warningly to restrain me from jumping up and running off to tell the glad news to all the folk of Jarrow.

"The very same," he said, "But travelling incognito."
"In cognito!" I cried, "How wonderful!"
I could hardly breathe for happiness. My heart was beating like a steam engine with a broken governor.
"There in my makeshift boat she danced and sang. The golden-haired moppet who has won the hearts of all the world."
"That's what she'd do," I said, "She'd dance and sing whatever danger threatened."
"She kept us going all through that dreadful night," mused Uncle Freddie.
"In her films she keeps everybody's spirits up. She's never afraid," I cried.
"The other lifeboats gathered round us. It was more like an outdoor concert than the greatest maritime disaster of the century," declared Uncle Freddie.
"Oh, how wonderful!" I breathed, "What did she sing?"
"What didn't she sing?" challenged the gallant survivor of the Titanic, "On the Good Ship Lollipop?"
"Of course! She'd have to sing that!"
"At the Codfish Ball?"
"'They'll all be there from the herring to the whale'," I sang.
"You've got to S-M-I-L-E?"
"To be H-A-double P-Y," I responded.

Uncle Freddie sat back in his chair, a good deed accomplished in a naughty world. Yet still a tiny trickle of doubt disturbed me.
"How wasn't it in all the papers, Uncle Freddie?"
"Shirley didn't want to be made out to be a great heroine," said my Uncle Freddie, promptly.
"But everybody should know how brave she was! The King should give her a medal," I declared, "I shall write to Buckingham Palace immediately."
His face became very solemn.
"All us survivors are sworn to secrecy, old son, because Shirley wasn't supposed to be there," he said, "You wouldn't have me break my sworn word, would you?"
I shook my head.
"What did she say, Uncle Freddie? Please try and remember what she said to you."
Plop, plop! Plop, plop, went his pipe. From deep within his capacious memory he drew the golden words the world's sweetheart had entrusted to him.
"I was sitting at the tiller I'd made from a tea tray and a deck tennis post, and she stood in front of me, and put one hand on each of my shoulders to steady herself...there was a fair swell that night...and she said, 'Freddie Dean, old bean, you must keep my secret forever and never let on to a living soul that I have been here.'"

"To the death!" I cried, "Her secret is safe with us!"
"My very words," said Uncle Freddie, "I said to her, very respectful."
I said, "You're always very polite. Even to the pollis."
"How can I tell you what she said if you keep interrupting?" cried my Uncle Freddie.
"Sorry."
"'Miss Temple,' I said. 'Call me Shirley, please,' she said. 'Very well' I said, 'Shirley, your secret is safe with me. But you are the heroine of this frightful night and all the world should know you have saved the lives of these folk by your cheery smile and your happy singing and dancing.'"
I could restrain myself no longer.
"Then why doesn't she want everybody to know?"
"I'm coming to that," said Uncle Freddie, "If you'll let me get a word in edgeways."
"Sorry."
"'You are very kind,' said Shirley, 'But I must remain anomalous.'"
"What's that mean?"
Uncle Freddie sighed the sigh of a man whose patience is fraying at the edges

faster than an unravelling gansey. He gave me a reproachful glance.
"'The world must not know I have been here,' said Shirley, 'I could do no less to help, although I must say it has not been easy singing and dancing cheerily on a boat made out of deck chairs and canvas.' The lass was right about that. One awful moment when she was singing ANIMAL CRACKERS IN MY SOUP she nearly fell through into the soup."
"But you saved her, didn't you?" I cried, the vision of Shirley Temple slipping through the flimsy structure into the Arctic depths never to sing Polly Wolly Doodle again being almost too much to bear.
"I grabbed her by the elbow and she smiled her thanks without interrupting her song. That's the sort of champion lass she is."
"You can tell that from her pictures," I said, "No matter what earth-shattering disaster she is facing she's always cheery and never loses heart. But why must she remain anomalous?"
Uncle Freddie answered readily, "'But why,' I asked her, 'must no one know of your heroism this tragic night?' 'Because,' she said, and there was more than a hint of sadness in her voice, 'Because I am under contract to Twentieth Century Fox and must not give unauthorised performances or otherwise my contract will be curtailed.'"
"Is that bad?" I asked anxiously, "To be curtailed?"
"As bad as it gets," said my Uncle Freddie grimly, "No more Shirley Temple pictures. Not ever."
"Not ever?" I cried.
"Not ever," said Uncle Freddie with a brow like thunder, "Total finito."
"Then I'll never say a word. I promise. Not even to my dying day."
"Good lad," he said warmly.
I asked, "What happened then?"
"There and then she picked a bottle of champagne from a crate that happened to be floating by and up she stands. 'It is with great pleasure,' she says, 'that I name these deck chairs THE GOOD SHIP LOLLIPOP and may all who cling to them be safely rescued before the curl comes out of my hair.' Wallop, goes the bottle! Hip, hip, hooray, go all the lifeboats! You could've heard the cheers as far as Timbuctoo."
"As far as that?"
"Possibly as far as Timbucthree," my revered relation assured me.

Uncle Freddie sat peacefully on the kitchen chair and sucked his empty pipe, undisputed champion storyteller of the world, even as far as Timbucthree. Plop, plop! I too breathed a sigh of deep contentment.
"In the morning we were picked up by the CALIFORNIAN and I've never seen

her from that day to this. But before she left she whispered into my ear, 'Farewell, Freddie Dean! We shall not meet again. But I shall never forget you. Will you forget me?'"

"Never!" I cried, my heart pounding.

"And then she kissed me," said Uncle Freddie, playing his trump card. "Where did she kiss you?" I cried, "Show me. Show me where Shirley Temple kissed you!"

Uncle Freddie lowered his weather-beaten face for my inspection and pointed out the very spot where the angel had blessed his cheek. There were no visible signs of osculation.

"I try not to wash it," explained that gallant gentleman, "But mum's the word, Lecky, old scone. I would not wish your Auntie Bella to know that I had been kissed by another. However world-famous the giver, a kiss is still a kiss." Ineradicable, indelible until the day you die. And don't you forget it.

"Mum's the word," I answered.

In my head I could see the arctic scene and hear the sweet voice that soothed the anxious soul and calmed the fearful heart. I heard the seabirds cry and saw the lifeboats dark-huddled about the fragile frame where the Hollywood nightingale sang, and my Uncle Freddie kept the teatray tiller by the Pole star.

Thus it came to pass that we were sitting peacefully in the sun, musing on the amazing, but true story related herein when two strangers, two well-dressed women entered the Place and front doors slammed like a twenty-one gun salute.

Had I but glimpsed the stomach-churning fate that the ladies' appearance portended for the hapless inhabitants of Hurworth Place I would've seized Uncle Freddie's hand and run for our front door. But we stayed put, unaware that in the guise of these ladies Fate was even now stretching out its sticky fingers to entrap the innocent.

"Aye-aye, old son. Trouble for some poor folk," concluded Uncle Freddie. If he could spot the juggernaut's approach why didn't we run and hide behind our sunblistered door? Why did we sit like rabbits under the steamroller?

"Well," I said, "They're not the tallywife. I've never seen one dressed like that." The tallywife was harder than the tallymen. She had to be. Mrs. McGuire never had any trouble with her club until she had the tallywife come round for the money. Every week the tallyman would stop at number seventeen for a pot of tea and afterwards walk away up the flags smiling which was unusual as a tallyman's smile was as likely as a convoy of dodos in Hurworth Place. Lily McGuire had roller skates and was promised a dolly for Christmas, but when the tallywoman started coming the McGuires had to do a flit. Lily McGuire left Hurworth Place holding the cart tail, riding on her skates and blowing kisses with her free hand, which I thought a very impressive exit.

"They're ladies," I told Uncle Freddie, speaking from a breadth of experience gained from much perusal of clothing club catalogues, "They're dressed like the pictures in Littlewoods."
"They could be the Means," appraised Uncle Freddie, "Though mind they look a bit too la-di-da for that."

It seemed that Hurworth Place had gone deaf although there were eyes behind every shabby net curtain. Jarrow had grown wary of authority in those days of the Poor Law and the Means Test when cockroaches in bowler hats and suits with shiny bums came round to measure poverty with a cruel tape.

"Charity," said Uncle Freddie, "That's who they are."

The cockroaches were followed by the ladies from the Charity, smelling of lavender water, who only meant to help, but only made matters worse with their haphazard largesse.

"Charity," repeated Uncle Freddie and made to spit, but changed his mind. He's promised Auntie Bella he wouldn't encourage me in bad habits and a promise is a promise. I wish he hadn't promised. I needed professional tuition. I could hit nothing but my own boots.
He said bitterly, "If they are, they're worse than the Means."
"How's it worse? Charity. How's it worse?"
"They want gratitude."

Defeated by the intransigence of the Place the ladies were now considering whether to approach us. Uncle Freddie said quietly, "It's as well your Dad's abed."

My father, the one-legged man of uncertain temper, who kept us by kneading the dough and feeding the ovens nightly at the Co-op Bakery would've broken anyone in half who suggested he was crippled, and therefore, a suitable case for charity. Anything a two-legged man could do, Davie Ferguson could do better on one leg. He was a proud and angry man. His brothers died on the Somme in 1916 and I believe he sometimes wished to have died with them. Our Mam and Auntie Bella might wash other folks' clothes and scrub their floors and Granny

Fergie unpick seams and sew for endless hours, but Our Dad was our principal bread-winner.

The ladies sailed towards us as stately as galleons upon a mirrored ocean.

"No retreat," said Uncle Freddie, "And no surrender."
They weren't the rent or the tally. They were easy. You lie like good soldiers out of sight and shrapnel under the window's parapet with your Mam's sweet breath in your ear so he can't see you when he presses his pig's snout against the glass. That was a great lark, outwitting the enemy. Also a great comfort lying on the lino with Our Mam or Auntie Bella's arms about me and a sweet carbolic-smelling hand over your mouth when a fit of giggles becomes too much. If you don't think good soldiers dream of their Mam's sweet breath in their ear when they're under bombardment I tell you they surely do. Uncle Freddie told me.

Hurworth Place was empty except for Uncle Freddie and me sitting in state, a state of tension.

"Heads down, old son," Uncle Freddie said, "Starshells up!"

The ladies smelled like the countryside smelled. Even under my tinhat I knew the younger lady was smiling at me.

"Good afternoon to you, sir," said the older lady to Uncle Freddie, "Isn't this weather marvellous? Although perhaps a trifle humid?"

She was an American. A Yankee. Which explained why she couldn't speak properly. Had these two ladies come all the way across the herring pond specially to ask our opinion of the weather?

Uncle Freddie said nowt. He sat as still as he'd showed me how they froze in No Man's land when the starshells went up. It was Uncle Freddie and me out beyond the front line stringing wire. Up went the starshells. Bang, bang, bang! Every man jack of us frozen still. Don't move, bonny lad. Chin on ya chest 'til the starshells die and the blessed dark returns. Listen for your Mam's sweet breath, and think like a tree stump.

"I said, good afternoon, sir. Don't you answer when a lady speaks to you?"

The older inquisitor sighed deeply. The same compassionless sigh that echoed through the dungeons of Torquemada. What she thought of Jarrow folk showed in the nettle of her voice. It was an infinitely patient, impatient voice. She would've much preferred to win Uncle Freddie's attention by kicking him sharply in the ankle.

"Little boy," sang the American Beauty rose, "Little boy, is your father deaf?"
"I'm not a little boy," I said.
"Aw, gee, sorry," sang the American blue jay, "I do apologise. What should I call you?"
The older lady sighed like a restless mare.
"Young man," she said, "We only wish to speak to you. We are not selling brushes door to door!"
The younger woman laughed and said, "Maybe we should, Rose. It sure can't be any harder."

I sneaked a look from under the rim of my tin hat into a dazzling shrapnel burst of wide blue eyes. Uncle Freddie sucked his empty pipe oblivious to eyes of a startling hue, a heavenly smile, and the scent of summer flowers. Seemingly deep in thought he pondered upon the meaning of life, the origin of the universe and the price of bacon.

"Why won't anyone speak with us, soldier?" the younger lady pleaded.
The old codfish said, "Really, Mary, it's all too tiresome. Neither he nor his father is deaf. They're just too rude and ill mannered to reply. Why on earth we bother I don't know. I shall make sure Mr. Kennedy is aware of the difficulties we face."
"Please give me a moment more, Rose," urged Mary of the azure eyes, "I swear I saw a flicker of life there."

What this sweet namesake of my mother saw was me struggling on the brink of falling in love with her. I made the mistake of looking up again. This Mary clasped a large notebook. Anyone with a notebook couldn't be on our side. Authority has a notebook and a forked tail. But a notebook, blue eyes and a halo of golden hair?

Life is full of confusions. Mr. Pollitt had warned us in Sunday School to beware of the Maiden who is fair of face, but whose heart hides Satan's snares. This wasn't a very young woman, but who knew what age the Maiden would be? Was this such a Maiden now, smelling so sweetly, smiling so beguilingly, transforming Hurworth Place with the radiance of her presence? If she was Satan's handmaiden he was certainly going to a lot of trouble just to catch Uncle Freddie and me.

Mr. Pollitt had green teeth and fish breath that were no recommendation for virtue and his wife had a face like an old cupboard door, sunblistered and flaking. She poked her nose when she wasn't playing the chapel organ and there was no room in her pinched cardigan for any of Satan's snares. You'd've seen the wires and pegs for sure. Worse still when it was too late I found out their Sunday School treat wasn't anywhere near as good as the Baptists who always had the best cream horns. Next year I'm going back to the Baptists.

Mr. Pollitt may have been safe from Satan's noose, but I felt my feet slipping from the strait and narrow way. If my heart were not already pledged to the golden moppet who has already featured in this true story of love and terror I would've drowned without a struggle in those eyes of cerulean blue. The Cerulean Sea is a dangerous shore for the untried heart.

"Yes, I surely did! There's someone alive in there," Mary cried, and reached out an alabaster arm to rap on my tin hat, "Hello in there? Is anyone home?"

I hated people knocking on my tin hat. Our Dad was the worst. He would strike matches on me and even stub out his Woodbine. When I sat in the safe shadow of Granny Fergie's knees even she would knock rat-a-tat with her knitting needle and ask if Danny Daydream was at home. I was anybody's drum kit.

"There's nobody home, miss," I answered, "We're all out, miss."

"You see, Mary! Even the children are accomplished in insolence," trumpeted Mrs. Rose Kennedy, whose husband would become the U.S. Ambassador to the Court of St. James and subsequently advise his President that the British were finished. They were too pigheaded to come to an accommodation with Hitler, yet too cowardly to fight and wouldn't last six weeks if they did. Any materiel given to the British would be wasted or a gift for the Wehrmacht. The Kennedy family skedaddled in November 1940, disappointed by the postponement of Operation Sealion.

Are you surprised to find Mrs. Rose Kennedy in this story? We had all the famous folk come to Jarrow when I was a child. They buzzed round Uncle Freddie like bees round a sticky bear. Why was that, d'y'think?

"There's no answer to such nonsense," proclaimed the matriarch of the Kennedy clan, "It's too hot. My feet are tired, and to be perfectly honest, honey, these people don't deserve our help. They're certainly not prepared to help themselves. Apathy! Sloth! Ignorance! Indiscipline! Sadly these are the keynotes of the British character today."

Uncle Freddie stirred, and said, in a voice of iron, "We don't want your charity, missus. We don't want your company either. Haddaway back to Yankeeland, and feed your own! For a start yi could let the black man on the tram and his lass in the shop where you buy your own baloney! I know your kind! I saw yi in France! All gob and wind! Away with yi afore I say something in front of the bairn I'll regret!"

The silence was painful. I felt sorry for the lady. Uncle Freddie's rare anger was frightening. Mary and I looked at one another solemnly like chastened children. I put my hand on his knee and felt the anger drain from him. He chewed on his empty pipe.

"Leave us be, missus," invited Uncle Freddie, "We'll manage fine without yi."
"Come away, Mary," Mrs. Kennedy sniffed, "We're well answered. There's nothing we can do to help these people."
"Give me a moment, please," begged Mary. She was not the false Maiden of fair countenance with her cardigan full of brass snares of pain. She was a spunky woman, not much younger than Our Mam who wasn't afraid of spiders and could bait her own hook.
"Soldier boy, please tell your father..." began Mary.
"I'm not really a soldier," I said, "This is my Uncle Freddie. Our Dad's asleep upstairs. He has to work nights."

Mrs. Kennedy's snort echoed the fussing shunter beyond Albert Road. Did she think Our Dad was a midnight mechanic? They weren't too keen to let them on the tram. Or in the shop. They had to travel on the back step where the wind would blow the smell away and send a passing bairn into Porter's for their Woodbines.

"Okay, okay," said the sweet American Beauty rose, "Please tell your uncle... Uncle Freddie that we haven't come all this way to insult him. I'm sorry if it sounds like that. This is Mrs. Rose Kennedy. The Kennedys are a very important family in the States. I'm Mary Pickford. We're from S.T.'s Trust and we're trying to find former employees of Palmer's Shipbuilding & Ironworks."

"S.T.?" I cried, "Did you say S.T., miss?"

If I had not been struck blind on the road to Damascus I would've realised I was speaking to Mary Pickford, America's Sweetheart. But what I saw in a blinding flash was who had sent these ladies. I knew a certain someone, S.T. herself, had not forgotten the TITANIC and now...

"Uncle Freddie!" I cried, "It's S.T.! You know! S.T.! You've got to listen!"

I shook Uncle Freddie so hard he nearly fell from the kitchen chair, and the pipe went in and out of his mouth like an unruly piston. His anger had already evaporated and blown away like a wet sponge in the Sahara.
I was frantic for his attention.
"Don't go away, miss," I begged, "My Uncle Freddie worked for Palmer's as a shipwright. Freddie Dean. He's the one you wanted. He's the one that sank the TITANIC."
The blonde lady with the cornflower blue eyes consulted her notebook.
"You're quite right, soldier," she smiled, and then, as if some angelus had rung, recited her litany over Uncle Freddie's bowed, unheeding head, "Let me introduce myself properly, sir. I am Mary Pickford. You may have heard of me? No? Well, never mind. I am here this summer as a voluntary worker for the S.T. Trust, and I am here to help you. S.T.'s Trust is American ..."
"I know that," I said smugly.
"Mrs. Kennedy and I are here with the support of the Embassy of the United States of America to extend our program of aid to your area. S.T.'s Trust is supported by many prominent people both here and in the States who wish to remain anonymous..."
"I know about that too," I said, "You wouldn't want to be curtailed."
"...while doing something practical to help their fellow men. Anonymous means we do not disclose their names."
"And in cognito too," I suggested helpfully.
"And incognito too, I guess. S.T. prefers not to attract publicity."
"Uncle Freddie's already sworn," I said, "And I've sworn this afternoon as well."
Mary Pickford regarded me curiously, but continued to recite her litany.
"So we are here as a Helping Hand across the Water, and if you would speak with us then perhaps we could assist you in this difficult time. That's what S.T. wants."

She fell silent having reached the bottom of the pamphlet's page where the footnote suggested she await a response. I gave her a worthy response. I nearly pulled Uncle Freddie's arm from its socket as I rocked him like a runaway cradle.

"Please, Uncle Freddie, please, listen to her! It's S.T.! You know! ESSSS TEEEE! The one whose name we are sworn never to mention to our dying day!"
"Don't talk daft," cried Uncle Freddie, uncomfortably hoist with his own petard.

"I'm not," I cried in anguish, "I'm sure it's her. She wouldn't do us any harm."
"I surely wouldn't," Mary Pickford assured me, grasping at straws. Uncle Freddie was as immovable as Marsden Rock. My pleas made as little impression on his stony stubbornness as the cries of the kittiwakes on the limestone crags. Mrs. Kennedy sighed again like Souter horn.
"Well, you have more patience than I have, Mary. I'm near to washing my hands of these people," she exclaimed wearily.
"Whoa back, missus," said Uncle Freddie, "'These people'? Who'd'y'think you're talking to? We don't grow cotton round here."
Mrs. Kennedy turned her imperial glare upon him before which generations of Kennedys would quail, but which only provoked a shake of the head from Uncle Freddie.
"What are you?" said that decent man, gently, "Third generation Irish? Yi've hardly got your feet out of the peat bogs. And you've forgotten already?"
"When you've endured sufficient impertinence, Mary," said Mrs. Kennedy, "you will find me at the car with the children. Please don't be too long. You know how fretful Teddy becomes."
Thus saying she turned on her heel, leaving Hurworth Place, unmourned, forever. Lily McGuire made a better, braver exit on her skates.

Uncle Freddie raised his empty pipe in salute and applauded her departure with, "Well, it's been grand having you here, missus. Remember my Granda to your Granda! They picked taties together."
Mary Pickford stood, a confusion of blue eyes and golden hair, looking down into her latticed fingers, bowed, but bloodyminded.
She said, doggedly, "She is a trifle hard to bear, sir, I do agree. But her heart is in the right place, I do assure you. She's just hot and tired. However, I'm Miss Yankee Grit and I volunteered to help and you won't chase me away so easily."
Eagerly I urged Uncle Freddie, "Please listen to her. For S.T.'s sake."

What could my Uncle Freddie say without tearing the timorous fabric of our fantasy life apart? What else did we have in that bleak little, sweet little, sooty little town, but the world of dreams he had created for me? So he clamped his lips about the empty pipe and subjected his boots to a rigorous examination.

"My!" smiled Mary Pickford, amused and mystified, "Do you know about S.T. and S.T.'s Trust, soldier boy?"
"Oh, yes," I assured her, "I know everything there is to know. I know all about S.T. and why you were sent here. I know who sent you all right. But my lips are sealed. Even unto my dying day. And probably longer."

As a child I was accustomed to implausible situations because Auntie Bella and I rapaciously devoured tuppenny romances such as VOW OF SILENCE, cuddled together on her kitchen fender in a cocoon of dread anticipation.

Have you read VOW OF SILENCE? You should. On page one hundred and twenty we found out it was brave Alistair's half-brother, the treacherous Terence who struck down the fair Amelia, her beauty o'er-shadowed by her cloak, thinking her to be stout Betty Boyle, the deaf mute who was carrying the ransom of gold to that dread, dripping cavern on the wild fells where the false cleric, the irreverent Browdie holds hostage the Squire's children, Arnold and Bennett. Betty Boyle thought she was carrying the Squire's bastard baby to old Mrs. Gangreen to be circumvented. Are you following the story so far?

But it was true Alistair who was sworn to silence lest disgrace fall upon his father's old grey head. Though Amelia's eyes pleaded with him from the pillow where her fair head lay, skin whiter than the fullered linen itself, to declare the truth and disclose the turncoat Terence. Instead Alistair gave one last loving glance to that pale paralysed maiden he adored and went out into the hallway where the Sheriff awaited to take him down to Balligibberish Gaol there to await execution. Auntie Bella and I were heartbroken.

Our only comfort is the eighty pages of VOW OF SILENCE we still have to read and grieve over. We read aloud taking turns as one finds a cinder in the eye or can carry the emotional fardel no further. Our relief at every romance's happy ending is immeasurable. The curious way I write and talk is all due to the education I received at Chatter & Windows Romantic Academy.

Mary Pickford laughed.
"What's your name, soldier?"
"My name is Alexander Young Ferguson, but everybody calls me Lecky. So I suppose you can as well."

I looked sideways at the inscrutable sphinx who had once been my loquacious Uncle Freddie, but there was no help forthcoming. However I suspected that while he was considering how many angels might dance on the head of a pin he was also listening to our conversation with some slight interest.

"Lecky? Lecky. Well, I guess that's kinda cute. You know who I am, don't you? Mary Pickford? I used to work in pictures."

She had been in the presence of the golden-haired moppet who had won the hearts of all the world? I was as awe-filled, as humbled as any mediaeval pilgrim viewing the grisly bits and bobs of sacred bones on the street vendor's tray. Had I not been seated on my beer crate I would've fallen to my knees in homage. I nudged Uncle Freddie to ensure his attention, dived into the blue pool of her eyes, and asked, "Do you...do you help with S.T.'s pictures?"

The angelic face of America's Sweetheart clouded with confusion. Then she laughed, groped for understanding, and answered, "Well, now, that's not really my province. I know there is quite a collection, but...Really, Lecky, honey, you are a remarkable kid! How did you know about the pictures?"
"I've always known," I answered, modestly. They have posters outside the Kino.
"Well, now, this is what I'm going to do. I'm going to explain everything to you because I don't want your good Uncle to shout at me when all I wish to do is help. Then after I'm gone. Well, he can do whatever he chooses."

She didn't need to explain it to me. I knew who S.T. was. You've guessed, haven't you? Shirley Temple. She'd sent us help just when we needed it most. Well, I was prepared to keep mum and say S.T. instead of Shirley Temple if that was the way S.T. wanted it. But she didn't fool me.
"Now this may surprise you, Lecky, honey, but..."
Nothing Mary Pickford could say would surprise me. On the other hand I might've been surprised if anyone had explained that it was Samuel Tilden, the American philanthropist, who had set the movement under way by financing the New York Free Library at a time when providing free books for the unwashed proletariat would have raised liberal laughter in many a gentleman's club. He also opened his gallery of pictures to the workingman. Ask Norman Richardson to let you look up Tilden in his Children's Encyclopaedia. It's all true. Every word. Good old S.T.!

"...good old S.T. has decided that the best way to help you, and avoid giving offence by the offer of cash money is to assist families with basic grocery needs. Can you read, Lecky, honey?"

I was mortified. Not only could I not remember a time when I was unaware of S.T.'s pictures I could not remember ever being unable to read. I had swallowed the printed word along with Our Mam's milk and perused the newsprint tablecloth whilst being spoon-fed at the kitchen table. I gave Mary Pickford a reproachful glance from which even angel eyes and golden hair couldn't defend her.

"I'm a better reader than any in Standard Seven. The teacher won't let me read now. She's just jealous. And Our Dad says if I wasted less time reading."
The teacher wouldn't let me read because I wouldn't stop.
"Okay, okay," Mary's hands calmed the troubled sea, "I'm sorry. Then take a look at this, Lecky, honey. Who knows, perhaps your Uncle Freddie may care to take a look-see also?"

What she put into my hands was a book of tickets. It smelled new and unopened. On the cover was a picture of two hands grasping one another above a wave-tossed ocean. This heavenly apparition must've frightened the living daylights out of the steamship crews passing to and fro below. In big letters it said, HANDS ACROSS THE SEA.

In smaller print it said: A TRANSATLANTIC PROJECT TO AID THE DISTRESSED, FINANCED BY THE S.T. TRUST, NEW YORK & LOS ANGELES, AND SPONSORED BY THE EMBASSY OF THE UNITED STATES OF AMERICA. I put this declaration of our dependence under Uncle Freddie nose, but he stared into space.

I whispered to him, urgently, "It is S.T. It really is!"

The sweet tones of America's Sweetheart intruded on my pleading.
"Let me tell you something about the scheme while you study the booklet, Mr. Dean. Unlike many schemes S.T.'s Trust places no restrictions upon the use of the vouchers."

The tickets were very pretty. There was a coloured picture of a big cream horn like the Baptist Sunday School Treat with all sorts of groceries falling out of it. A pair of anonymous hands grasping the horn showered its plenty onto to a smiling lady showing off her teeth who looked just like Mary Pickford. There was a lad with freckles and a lass with golden plaits and big grins on their faces while all the stuff fell on their Mother without them lifting a finger to help. I was disappointed there wasn't a picture of Shirley herself.

There is on the Gazette SMILERS' CLUB certificate. Shirley Temple is the president of our Club. She takes a personal interest in all her members. It says so in the letter Uncle Eric writes you when you join. Well, she was certainly taking a personal interest in Uncle Freddie and me.

Mary Pickford was gaining confidence from Uncle Freddie's silence.

"To save time let me read you what it says inside the cover. Would you mind if I did just that?"
"Suit yourself," said Uncle Freddie, but I could tell he was interested.
"It says, and I quote: 'Mr. Shopkeeper, each voucher in this booklet has a value of twenty shillings English money or five U.S. dollars."
I was astonished.
"Twenty shillings each? For each ticket? Not for the lot?"
"That's right, Lecky, honey," she answered brightly, "In English money, twenty shillings. I'm sure that's correct."
I savaged Uncle Freddie's arm, tearing it from the socket.
"She said a pound! A pound each!"
Uncle Freddie took the book of tickets from my hand and started reading for himself. Mary Pickford solemnly winked at me and continued to read aloud.

"...And we would ask you to accept the vouchers at their face value in exchange for grocery purchases. There are no restrictions on purchases except that of tobacco and alcohol. No cash change should be given except of the smallest amount, as it is not the intention of the Trust that these grocery vouchers should be redeemable for cash money. The vouchers are redeemable by the retailer at full face value at any branch of the Northern Provincial Bank."

We were rich beyond our wildest dreams! I gaped at Uncle Freddie. In the mirror of his eyes I saw the reflection of my own astonishment.
Uncle Freddie asked cautiously, "Just how soon can we...?"
America's Sweetheart blossomed with girlish delight and cried, "Why, just as soon as you, Mr. Frederick William Dean, sign my inventory right here, and sign your name inside the cover of the voucher booklet in my presence."
"I've no pen," admitted Uncle Freddie, shamefacedly, "Wi've not much call for pen and ink writing in Hurworth Place."

D'y'think that's a definition of poverty? To be without the means to express love and sorrow? To know only the plebeian pencil and the rude indelible in the rent book? How many mute inglorious Miltons lived out their time in Albert Road and never knew the Paradise they lost? How many Will Shakespeares never penned comparisons with a summer rose for lack of pen and ink? That's poverty.

Uncle Freddie offered to return the vouchers with a reluctant hand. I stared at him aghast. Our mother lode had turned to iron pyrites. The luxury of Havana gave way to the bronchial wheezing of the old shunting engine. Uncle Freddie looked at me helplessly.

I stayed his hand and cried, "Wait! Tommy Capstick's got pen and ink! Don't go away, miss! Please!"
"Whoa back there, soldier! I have a pen," exclaimed our benefactress, "Please, Mr. Dean, be my guest."

It was my first view of a fountain pen, a big fat Waterman that winked with gold in the sunlight. Slowly, carefully, with his tongue sticking out and reaching for his nose, Uncle Freddie wrote his name twice, on the inventory and on the voucher booklet.

"Thank you," sang the American thrush, and fell back into her pamphlet voice, "Please keep the vouchers in a safe place. It is S.T.'s intention."
"God bless her!" I cried, unable to restrain myself.
"...to help your family through the difficulties of the next twelve months and so you will find forty vouchers in the booklet, each with a value in English money of twenty shillings or five dollars American. A thrifty housewife will be able, I am sure."
Uncle Freddie, choking with astonishment, cried out, "Forty chittees! Why, miss, that's...that's!"
"Forty pounds," I assured him, being top at mental arithmetic even if Miss Kettle said I was too clever by half, always interrupting, "Forty pounds in proper money."

The pipe dropped from his nerveless lips and I was able to have a good suck at it, thus achieving one of my earliest ambitions in life. Until a bewildered Uncle Freddie searching for solace absently pulled the pipe from my mouth as one might pull a cork from a bottle to return it to his own. He sat staring at the fortune in his trembling hands.

I knew Our Dad would've torn up the voucher booklet with its false fraternity and overflowing cornucopia without a moment's hesitation, and never regretted it. The only things he ever wanted They couldn't give back. His brothers and his leg, lost in Flanders. He wanted nothing else that he couldn't earn by the sweat of his brow. That was Our Dad. My Uncle Freddie was different.

And so the golden girl, Mary Pickford, America's Sweetheart, came into my life, lingered a moment and left. And I scarcely noticed. She had recently divorced Douglas Fairbanks, but I was too young for her anyway. Besides my heart was pledged to another. But that was life in Jarrow when I was but a scabby-kneed bairn, famous folk came and went as regular as the Shields tram.

No sooner had Mary Pickford departed for the shining motorcar where Mrs. Kennedy grudgingly fed Teddy the milk of human unkindness than Uncle Freddie sighed deeply and admitted, "Too late now, old son," thus acknowledging his fall from grace.

No sooner had America's Sweetheart vanished, leaving the summer air shimmering with an after-image of bright blue eyes and a hint of American Grit, than Uncle Freddie tore the book of grocery vouchers in two. Not in half. Down the middle.

"Here ya, old sausage," he said, and to my uncomprehending gaze, "Hide them. Tuck them away somewheres safe."
I started to say, "You know Our Dad won't let."
But he interrupted with "Who said anything about your Dad? I know Davie Ferguson. You keep them for your Mam. Mams have a different way of looking at things."

The way Our Mam would perch her head on one side like a sparrow and look at me sometimes? That look was sharper than any bird's beak. She would smile and her beauty filled my head with rainbow bubbles. Then she would say, "I can see right inside your head, Our Lecky, and there's a big black fib sitting there. Would'y'like iss to hoick it out afore it turns septic on yi?"

"I won't tell any fibs about it, Uncle Freddie."
He gave me a reproachful look that filled my mouth with ashes of shame.
"When did I ask yi to?" he queried gently, "They might just come in handy. Give them to your Mam. But hide them for now."

With a certain misgiving I hid the vouchers among my other treasures in the pigeonholes of my beer crate. In later years when questioned about this dubious episode, Uncle Freddie would simply tap his nose twice, and solemnly utter these words, "Noblesse obliged!" to which Our Dad would rudely respond, "Noblesse be buggered!"

"Right then, old squirt," he said, determination gathering pace, "We're away up to the Store to get something for your Mam and Bella's tea."
"We've no money," I answered.
"No money?" he exclaimed, riffling the voucher booklet under my nose; the Yankee Mam and her bairns juggled desperately with the cascade of eggs and milk, "These are better than money. Don't yi think your Mam deserves a treat?" In this fashion he ensnared me as a witless accomplice.
"More than anybody," I said fiercely, "More than anybody in the whole world. Except Auntie Bella."

Never in my life have I shared a prouder moment than that magical afternoon when Uncle Freddie and I paraded up Albert Road to the Jarrow & Hebburn Co-operative Store with the charity vouchers burning a hole in his trouser pocket.

Kings and princes may think they walk in splendour, but no monarch promenaded more proudly than my Uncle Freddie in collarless shirt and braces, with the odd bairn that I was at his side, in tin hat and sockless boots. Up Albert Road to Humbert Street we marched and into the Store.

Once within its marble splendour we stopped and took a deep breath. Kubla Khan may have decreed a stately pleasure dome in Xanadu, but I doubt if it was any statelier than the Co-op Store, Humbert Street, Jarrow, where Alf, the scabby errand boy ran, past taverns measureless to man, down to the sunlit sea. At no extra cost to the customer.

All the unattainable luxuries of the world lay before us in this Aladdin's cave from bacon slicer through China tea to candied fruit. It was both terrifying and exhilarating. Of course, I had been in and out of the Store since conception, but never ever in the company of such as the ragged-trousered philatelist: an uncle of private ways and means.

To the dreamer of dreams by my side, to the disinherited prince and poet, Freddie Dean, it was a moment of paddy pride that toppled over into extravagance and folly. For what began in that Store in Humbert Street I never blamed my Uncle Freddie.

Some folks did. There were ugly rumours that had he been caught close to the crime they would've had him decorate a lamp post. It was as serious as that. How many they'd've made him decorate I cannot tell you. They were all sadly in need of a lick of paint. On some lamp posts in Albert Road you could still see the red-white-and blue from the Coronation of 1911.

We walked round the counters, savouring the smells and smelling all the savours. Cyril Liddell, custodian of this treasure house, was serving Mrs. Elliott. He always served the nobs did Cyril. He was offering fancy Mrs. Elliott a blob of butter on a palette knife and saying, in his voice like a snail's trail, "Try the Danish by all means, madam, there's some as prefers it" and after a respectful pause while her slobby gob sucked at the butter, "Well, it's not for me to say a word against the Danish, but personally I always prefer the home-produced myself. I'm not so sure that butter travels as well as wine. I've thought sometimes, hallo, Cyril, that's an odd flavour! Was it intended, I ask myself?"

What a wonderful thing to be a bon viveur, a gourmet, in a Philistine desert like Jarrow where we ate anything that stood still long enough.

My Uncle Freddie went to school with Cyril Liddell who was going to Go Far. He travelled all of half a mile from the schoolyard to the Co-op to weigh out tea and sugar. And in the course of time to rise to the position of Manager. Our Nancy worked at the Store when she first left school, but not for long. She used to bubble in the netty down the yard so's Our Mam wouldn't know. When I asked her under the door what was wrong, she said, "You are! So go away. There's nowt wrong," but I could hear that everything was wrong.

"You're quite right, madam," slimed Cyril, "Foreign! That's it exactly! If it's foreign I look twice. I really do. Now Empire and Colonial! Well, that's different, isn't it? I mean that's British after all!"

Mrs. Elliott sat in regal splendour on a chair bigger than wee Alice who ran like a timorous beastie to fetch and carry. I never heard Mrs. Elliott speak. I suppose she was capable of speaking, but she was too superior to speak to the general public. I never saw her smile. She conveyed her demands with frowns and pouts and gestures of disdain. She was cut from the same cloth as Mrs. Kennedy. Our Mam said she was a nasty piece of work and to keep well out of her reach. Mrs. Elliott was undoubtedly the Queen of Grange Ward and never forgot a slight, however slight. She weighed eighteen stone and if she'd fallen on you that would've been the end of yis.

"An admirable choice, Mrs. Elliott," gushed slimy Cyril, "It's a pleasure to serve a customer of such discerning taste. We use nothing else at home. Mother's very particular. It'll be the full pound, is it?"

He was using more than a pound just buttering up the old hagfish. Our Mam said a liddell bit of Cyril Liddell went a long way. Never mind the full pound. But Cyril Liddell plays an important part in this story. It was he who put the Lucifer to the gunpowder trail laid by Mrs. Kennedy. The presence of the odious Mrs. Elliott didn't help either.

"See owt y'fancy, old son?" asked Uncle Freddie expansively, "I was looking at the ham, but I'm thinking it's a bit ower fat for us. Not what I'd call a prime York ham. Very disappointing. Pricy too. For the quality."
I whispered, "Uncle Freddie, somebody'll hear you."
"Oh, and who would that be then?" he demanded as though speaking to the deaf.
"Cyril Liddell," I whispered.
"Who?" he demanded.
"Cyril Liddell, " I whispered through gritted teeth.
"Has the Co-op a new rule then?" he demanded.
I gaped at him.
"Like the Library is it? Customers have to keep their gobs shut. Unless spoken to. Is that it?"

I should've kept my gob shut. He was in a funny mood. It was a mistake to have spoken.

"Aye, well, we'll give the ham the go-by," he proclaimed generously, "But speak up, old sausage, if anything takes your fancy."
"Uncle Freddie," I whispered, convict-fashion from the side of my mouth, "I don't think we should be doing this."
"Expense is no object today, my old pudden. What's the point of a windfall, Lecky, old jampot, if we don't enjoy the breeze?"
I pulled him away to peruse a shelf of tinned peas.

"If you'll forgive my mentioning it, madam," declared the obsequious Cyril, laying it on with a trowel as prescribed by Disraeli, as he scanned the monster's shopping list, "But I was very pleased to read of Mr. Elliott's success in the Chronicle. You must be very proud of him. Of course, he's worked for it, hasn't he? Not like some of the shiftless I could mention."

His eyes fell for the briefest span upon Uncle Freddie's shoulder and fled when that gentleman turned to look at him.

"Our Arthur's doing very well in Reading," oozed Cyril, "Mother and I'll be down for our holidays next, I expect. Now is there anything I've missed? No, no, no. Yes, yes, yes. That's all your list, present and correct, madam. Now is there anything else I can tempt you to, Mrs. Elliott?"

Cyril Liddell had a head like a wrinkled balloon, a red balloon with a fringe of ginger hair, which wobbled insecurely on a tiny body and when he bobbed along behind the counter you looked for the bairn holding the stick. The softer-hearted might've felt it was a poor joke to give a bairn such an ugly balloon.

"Might I suggest a tin of fruit for Sunday tea, Mrs. Elliott?" slyed Cyril, "A well-earned treat. Perhaps a tin of Fruit Salad? Or Pineapple Chunks? A popular choice. Nothing more delicious. I'm sure you and Mr. Elliott are looking forward to a little celebration? A tin of shaky milk to add that final touch of luxury?"

"Now there's a thought," said Uncle Freddie, still speaking as though to a companion of impaired hearing, "Could I possibly tempt yi to a tin of fruit for our tea, eh, Lecky? Wha'd'y'think? A touch of the shaky milk? The lasses'd like that, eh? Coming in from scrubbing floors."

"A tin of fruit would be nice," I whispered, conscious of being both on holy ground and thin ice simultaneously, "Our Mam'd like that."
"Fruit Salad? Pineapple chunks?" he suggested gaily, "But let's not be overhasty. There's no hurry, old son, no hurry at all!"
Cowardly Lecky whispered, "I think Mr. Liddell's watching us."
"Is he now? Then we must make sure we give the Store the twice-over afore we buy owt," my genial uncle decided.

Breathe deeply. Can you smell that? The marvellous, mouth-watering, nose-rippling, tongue-tingling odour of a real shop. Go on, suck deep and savour the flavour of the Co-op. It's free. It's heavenly. It's gone forever. In those days shops smelled. Of bacon and pine sawdust underfoot. Of ripe cheese and China tea. Of pork sausage and paraffin. Oranges and coffee. Dried fruit and furniture polish. Firelighters and candles. Carbolic soap and freshbaked bread.

"No, no, that's no trouble, Mrs. Elliott, no trouble at all," squirmed slippery

Cyril, "Alfie'll have it round your door within the hour. Y'can count on that. Alfie! Alfie! Where's he got to now? By, but that lad wants chasing. Only too glad to be of service, Mrs. Elliott. Do be sure to give my congratulations to Mr. Elliott, mind!"

And thus did Mrs. Elliott depart the Store with Cyril at her elbow and wee Annie running like a hysterical harvest mouse behind the counters to get to the door in time.

You're wondering who this Mrs. Elliott is, aren't you? She's the wife of the Inspector of Police. All these years later creepy Cyril is still keeping in with Teacher.

And her husband's success? You're thinking he's tackled armed bank robbers single-handed, aren't you? Well, not quite. He broke up a gang of starving men who were stealing coal from a spoil heap. Real desperadoes. Seven of them went to prison and seven families went down into destitution. If you don't believe me, you can look it up. Only the names have been changed to protect the guilty. But it's not lost on Uncle Freddie. The fuse is burning.

"Well then, old son, wha'd'y'think, eh?"
We had stopped in front of the tinned fruit.
"About what, Uncle Freddie?"
"Well, Lecky, old scout," cried my bold Uncle Freddie, scarcely believing what he was saying, "I think we'll have ourselves a tin of pineapple for our tea? D'y'fancy pineapple chunks, old son? Would pineapple fit the bill then, d'y'-think?"

My Uncle Freddie loved pineapple. He lusted after pineapple. Succulent chunks of fruity flesh! The sticky liquor that pours tinny-tasting down the thirsting throat! Oh, bliss! Oh, paradise! Oh, pineapple!

"I don't know," I whispered weakly, "D'y'think we should?"

On the thighs of the tins there were dusky maidens holding out the world's biggest pineapple to hapless, hap'nnyless Lecky and smiling at him as no one had ever smiled before. Our Mam had never told me there'd be tins like this.

Uncle Freddie was outraged, his indignation almost visible.
"Yi don't know? Did I hear yi aright?"
I admitted sadly, "I don't know."

What I meant was, 'D'y'think we dare to taste life's forbidden fruit or should we scurry back to the bread'n'scrape of obscurity?'
"I shouldn't doubt," mused my Uncle Freddie, "But that King George and his lady wife, our Queen, God bless them, have pineapple chunks for tea regular as clockwork every Sunday. Then why shouldn't we, old sausage? In a land fit for heroes."

My daydream of King George, complete with crown, popping in to buy a tin of pineapple chunks and a tin of shaky milk was interrupted by Betty Robson saying, "Was yi wanting something, Freddie Dean?" very offhand, examining her nails for wildlife.

Betty Robson had a face like a suet pudden with a big mouth painted bright red where they tied up the pudden and pale eyes like you might find watching you slyly over the pigsty wall. It was Betty Robson made our Nancy's life a misery when she worked for the Co-op. Not that Cyril Liddell attempted to stop her.

Uncle Freddie's hard hand closed on mine like a vice.

"Aye, it's a tin of pineapple bits we're wanting for our tea, please."

It was the second time that day that I saw somebody look as if they'd been knocked down by the giant sausage falling from over Mr. MacAtominey's shop window. Betty Robson's fat red mouth fell open like a trap door. Had the waxy lips dropped off and hit the deck like Uncle Freddie's pipe I wouldn't have been surprised.

She recovered herself enough to sniff and say, "For a minute there I thought you said pineapple. I haven't time for games. D'y'want something or not?"
"There's nowt wrong with your hearing. Pineapple chunks. But I've changed me mind."
I looked at him with startled apprehension. In the ensuing pause, Betty Robson sighed languidly at her nails.
"We'll have two of them big tins," said my Uncle Freddie, without a tremor, "They'll go farther."

The fuse was in the barrel. Frustration is more dangerous than trinitrotoluene. I blame Betty Robson myself. Yes, Slimy Cyril and Mrs. Elliot bear some responsibility, but Betty could've nipped the fuse. Instead of assuming my Uncle Freddie could pay for what he wanted, or even waiting to find out he couldn't, when she could've dished out an even bigger helping of humiliation, she splashed him with contempt.

"Don't talk so daft! The likes of you cannot afford pineapple," accused Betty Robson, and then she shouted across to the cubicle, "Mr. Liddell, you're not gonna believe this! Freddie Dean wants pineapple chunks."

You could've cut the silence in the Store with a cheese wire. Every old wife had her ears cocked and her breath bated. Uncle Freddie had everybody's undivided attention. I was hoping the floor would slowly open up and we could slink into thankful oblivion. Even Mrs. Blagden who had never stopped talking since the night the Hun dropped the bomb on Palmer's fell silent.

Mr. Liddell's head popped out of his little glass office. Pee-boo! A red balloon on a stick. But where was the happy clown's face to follow?

"Did I hear you aright, Miss Robson?"
"Uncle Freddie," I whispered, "I think we should..."
He pressed my hand to silence.
"You heard me all right," Betty tittered, "This daft begger wants pineapple chunks for his tea. Did you ever hear anything like it?"

Her sniggers turned to laughter and one of the old hens cackled and then they all joined in, enjoying a really good laugh at Uncle Freddie's expense. Cyril Liddell had to wipe away the tears and blow his nose loudly.

"I think that'll be quite enough, Miss Robson," said Cyril, righteously, "There's customers want serving." Turning his attention to my Uncle Freddie, swelling with self-importance, he announced, "Whatever next? A tin of salmon, perhaps? You cannot have pineapple, Freddie. And that's final. You know where the door is."

I knew then that Cyril Liddell had made a big mistake. What I didn't realise was that Uncle Freddie was going to make an even bigger one. I mean, did they really expect him to turn and run when old Jerry couldn't shift him through all the muck and bullets?

"Who says I can't?" said Uncle Freddie, very quietly.

Cyril Liddell said, "I'm glad yi dropped in, Freddie. Best laugh I've had in years.

Have yi ever considered going on the halls? Man, yi'd top the bill no time. For sheer daftness. Away with yi!"

The old wives were having the time of their lives. Cyril struggled hard not to join the laughter, but had to turn away, shoulders shaking. Betty Robson was in hysterics, stuffing her hanky in her gob, hugging her generous bosom to avoid any damage to the structure. Uncle Freddie stood silent and immovable though I tugged at his hand with all the strength of a breaking heart.

But all good things must come to an end. Cyril Liddell, removing his specs to wipe away the frivolous tears with an apron corner, reverted to righteous indignation.

"I said away with yi, Freddie Dean! You're a regular daftie, man! I'll tell you what I will do for you though. Seeing as yi've given us a good laugh. I'll not tell your lass. I'll spare yi the clout on the lug Bella'd give yi for your antics."

Which generosity only dispatched Betty and the old wives to further hysteria while Cyril Liddell stood preening himself in the sunlight of their silly laughter.

I never liked Mr. Liddell. He never served bairns in their proper turn and when he did, he would grab your wrist, lick his indelible pencil and write the change on the back of your hand. He pressed hard to hurt. He knew he caused pain and he smiled his sly little smile.

Uncle Freddie waited until Betty Robson had mopped her streaming eyes and regained her breath. Then he repeated, politely, "I'll take two of your biggest tins of pineapple chunks if you'll be so kind," licking his thumb to open the book of S.T.'s chittees.

"Are yi drunk, man?" accused Cyril Liddell, "You're drunk. That's what's up with yi. Haddaway home and sleep it off afore I fetch the pollis!"

Through all the length of years I see my Uncle Freddie standing there, braving the laughter of the silly women, facing the contempt of malicious Cyril Liddell and the sniggering amusement of Betty Robson. I also see my cowardly self, near wetting myself with terror.

My Uncle Freddie reached across the counter to take Cyril Liddell by the collar.

He pulled him across the battered beech to a chorus of overall buttons. The Store was as silent as Tutankhamen's tomb.

"Smell my breath," said Uncle Freddie.
"I'll get the pollis ti yi," Cyril Liddell threatened.
"For what? For bad breath? Can yi smell owt but bread and scrape? Can yi?" Uncle Freddie demanded.
"No," Cyril Liddell agreed reluctantly, "No, I cannot."

Uncle Freddie let go and Cyril fell in a heap, vanishing below the counter, to rise, gasping and gulping, helped to his feet by Betty Robson who was staring at my Uncle like a surprised codfish.

"And you, Betty Robson, I know yi made our Nancy's life here a misery," Uncle Freddie declared with open contempt.
"Mr. Liddell," complained Betty Robson, "Are you just gona stand there and let daft Freddie Dean bla'guard iss?"
"Course he is," said Uncle Freddie, "He's no better than you. He's a coward and a bully too. Our Nancy's worth a dozen of your sort. You nipped and punched her out of her job. There was nobody here to help her."
When Betty's mouth wobbled in denial, Uncle Freddie said, "Oh, yes, yi did. Don't bother to deny it. So before I come round the counter ti yi I'm asking yi one last time to serve me. D'y'recognise me? I'm a customer. I'd like to be treated like one."

Betty's answer was to burst into tears, sobbing loudly, and Cyril Liddell who had stood white-faced, fumbling with his thumbs, blowing his nose, counting his buttons, put an arm round her and said timorously, "Y'should be ashamed, Freddie Dean, abusing a young lady!"
"A few tears won't do her any harm," said my Uncle Freddie, who was truly a gentle man, "Meanwhile, I won't buy two tins of pineapple. I've changed me mind."
"I thought you would," sniffed Cyril Liddell.
"I want every tin of pineapple yi've got," cried my Uncle Freddie, "Every last tin. All the bairns in Hurworth Place'll have their fill of pineapple today. Aye, Tommy Ashton's bairns'll have pineapple chunks for their tea. Instead of bread and water at his Majesty's displeasure like their Dad. Thanks to Inspector Elliott."

I heard the bugles blow in my head. The bonny drummer boys plied their sticks. My scalp tingled. The cavalry mounts snorted and stamped. The sharp breeze caught the pennants and spread the standard boldly. Death or Glory? The bugles blew the Charge. I could hardly breathe. Who else but Uncle Freddie would gallop headlong into such folly? The audience roared with delight. It was better than any pantomime at the Empire.

In a tearful voice, Betty Robson sniffed and snuffled, "And what're you gonna use for money, Freddie Dean? This is the Co-operative Wholesale Society. Not Hannan Ratty's. We don't take iron washers here."
Emboldened by the laughter from the stalls, Cyril added, "Or will we have the privilege of cashing your personal cheque, Freddie?"
Under the laughter I tugged him down to whisper, "Let's go, Uncle Freddie, please. What'll Auntie Bella say? What'll Our Mam think?"
"Stand fast, the Tyneside Scottish," whispered Uncle Freddie.

"Why, man, there must be," said Cyril, casting an eye on the shelves, "Twenty, no, twenty-five pounds worth of pineapple on these premises."
"Twenty pounds for the lot?" Uncle Freddie offered.
"Why not?," cried Cyril Liddell, sarcastically, "A bargain at the price!"
"Done then!" cried Uncle Freddie, "Twenty pounds it is!"
To an open-mouthed Cyril, he announced, "If yi'll just cast an eye on this, and then serve us without any further delay," he passed the charity vouchers over the counter with a regal gesture of indifference.
I gazed aghast and cried aloud, "Oh, Uncle Freddie, what have you done!" But it was too late.

When Cyril Liddell finished giving the booklet the once-over, twice-over, even the thrice-over, he admitted reluctantly, "Well, it all seems to be in order."

There was an audible intake of breath and then from the matinee audience a great shout of triumph arose to shake the rafters. Audiences are fickle creatures, are they not? Pale flakes of plaster fluttered from the ceiling.
Outside in the road a crowd, drawn by the revolutionary fervent within the Store, was gathering like the rain clouds above the river.

"If you're sure you know what you're doing," said Cyril Liddell, acknowledging defeat, not ungracefully, "But my advice to you would be."
"I can do without your advice," our local hero declared, "Now if yi'll see Alfie loads the cart I'll see it's returned."
"He's just got Mrs. Elliott's groceries loaded," Betty Robson complained.

"Then he'll just have to get them unloaded, won't he?" Uncle Freddie suggested.

Once outside in Humbert Street it was better than a royal visit. There was me and Uncle Freddie with the handcart piled high with pineapple tins, dozens upon dozens of dusky brown maidens proffering golden delights, the fruit of tropical sunshine, to half the population of Hurworth Place and Albert Road who hadn't seen anything better than bread and scrape and a mug of tea for months.

The sense of occasion infected even the miserable Liddell who, accompanied by the still-baleful Betty, actually came out of the Store onto the pavement. A ripple ran through the crowd. Such a thing had never happened before! A near-noble figure in his near-white apron, spectacles glittering in the summer sunlight, Cyril Liddell, with an abrupt gesture of his skinny arm brought the raging sea of the clamorous crowd to silence.

There on the pavement of Humbert Street, Cyril Liddell redeemed himself, pressing a parting gift upon Uncle Freddie, declaiming sonorously, "Freddie Dean, on this unique occasion when we have cleared the shelves of pineapple chunks, on behalf of the Jarrow and Hebburn Co-operative Society…": the more religious among the crowd hastily crossed themselves as he spoke those sacred words: "…on behalf of all of us with the C.W.S., I'd like you to accept this gift with our kindest regards!"

It was a bull's head tin opener. We have it still in our kitchen drawer.

Away we went rattling down Albert Road with a host of dusky maidens rotating their tums in time with the cartwheels on the cobbles. The bigger bairns ran ahead to spread the news of the approach of our hero's return. When we turned into Hurworth Place there on the flags were Our Dad, half-asleep and bewildered, Granny and Grandad and all the folk of the Place, all the bairns jumping up and down like rowing boats on a lipper.

"What's Auntie Bella going to say?" I asked.
"What can she say?" Uncle Freddie answered, "It's done."

Then everybody down to Doughty's dog was clamouring round us. Our Dad was still trying to prise out of Uncle Freddie what was going on when Grandad Fergie who was even more irresponsible than Uncle Freddie, but with a practical turn of mind, opened one of the big tins, thereby resolving the Gordian knot with one fell swoop of the bull's head tin opener.

Then the oohs and aaahs started as Grandad began popping sticky pineapple chunks into the bairns' gaping jaws. Then Our Dad gave up trying to make sense of what was going on and joined him, opening tins and filling gobs.

Granny Fergie sat on the kitchen chair sharing a tin of heavenly delight with mesdames, Chamberlain and Capstick while the other old wives went scooting for bowls and basins. Those with aspirations to gentility returned with forks and spoons. All the Dads and Grandads came outdoors, pulling up their manly braces, rubbing their sore eyes, sight for the use of, complaining about the unseemly din until they saw the dusky maidens on the cart. Then they shot back inside to get the old tin opener from the darkness of the table drawer.

That afternoon all of Hurworth Place went mad, literally mad for pineapple. Uncle Freddie was the hero of the golden hour as everybody stuffed his or her face with warm, sticky, heavenly, succulent chunks of pineapple flesh.

By the time Our Mam and Auntie Bella returned, hot and tired from scrubbing floors, the damage was done. It was easier for the weary women to accept a fait accompli and a dessert spoon apiece than to struggle against the fruity madness. Even the air over Hurworth Place hung heavy with the sickly sweet scent of pineapple. Which was a great improvement on how it smelled sometimes.

Every Hurworthian, every last half-starved bairn, biddy and ben, was gorging on pineapple. The babbas in their prams were sitting up and chewing for dear life or sucking bottles of ambrosial nectar. All their awful broodlings with their fluff-glued faces and mole-paw hands were gulping down the rare fruit or drowning in the sugary syrup. All the Mams and Grannies who had never seen such luxury since Mafeking, were smiling and cracking, spooning extravagantly, supping the nectar directly from the tins, careless of sticky chins, sisters to the dusky maidens sweating in the pineapple plantations. What bliss for the toothless! All the Dads and Grandads were stuffing their cheeks like dormice and cracking on how they marched to Jerusalem with their swords dragging in the sand when they weren't slashing pineapples from the pineapple palms, each and every one caught up in the ecstasy of the pineapple orgy.

It was the most blissful, stickiest, gorgingest, happiest, most heavenly afternoon Hurworth Place had seen since the Victory Celebrations of 1919 when they tried to burn down the Town Hall and fought the pollis to a draw. The Poor Law Board, the Means Test, the endless years of lay-offs, lock-outs and unemployment, the crippling poverty that mocked the dream of a land fit for heroes were all momentarily forgotten. For one brief moment of happiness the dark clouds lifted and the silver lining showed clean through.

Their boat had come in at last, and if they weren't having bloaters on silver dishies, they were, at least, bloated on pineapple, drunk on pineapple, up to their silly grins and sticky ears in pineapple. When the penultimate, ultimate choice chunk had been chewed and swallowed, the last slurp of syrupy nectar slurped, the final, smiling tin licked clean and dry, the terminal belch broken, the Last Post posted, it was too late for Auntie Bella to do much to Uncle Freddie. Except to smack his head, punch him in the chest as he backed off and try to kick him as he fled. Yet it was all rather half-hearted for such as the redoubtable Bella. Uncle Freddie was cheered to the echo as he adroitly dodged her blows to plant a juicy kiss on her cheek before fleeing the field of uneven combat.

If the greatness of a man is judged by the happiness he creates for his neighbours then surely had Uncle Freddie quit this mortal coil by tripping over an empty tin and striking the cobbles stone-dead there and then, the Pearly Gates would've swung open with a triumphant fanfare of trumpets to welcome home this sticky-fingered picaroon.

But he was too nimble on his feet for such a martyr's exit, and the sunlit afternoon passed into summer's evening as the contented folk of Hurworth Place sat sated and cracked on about the Great Treat, and its author, Freddie Dean, the Pineapple King of Jarrow.

It began in the early evening with just a little uneasiness. Just a little twinge. A little queasiness in the interior tubes. The backyard netties of Hurworth Place began to see a gradually increasing flow of traffic; always plainly audible through open kitchen windows on a hot summer night, with the flushes going, the doors banging and the shooting of the bolts.

If you are not too familiar with the sanitary arrangements of such havens of human habitation as Hurworth Place, perhaps, I should explain.

Hurworth Place consisted of little flats, with a family upstairs and a family downstairs, sharing one tap and one netty in the same backyard.

You might learn a lot about community spirit with two families totalling anything up to ten, twelve people sharing one toilet bowl. Or even fifteen or sixteen friendly backsides if you happened to be as lucky as Tommy and Ellie Capstick who had the Chamberlain tribe as neighbours.

I suppose in hindsight it was pretty obvious that half-starved folk who aren't accustomed to a wide and varied diet shouldn't suddenly stuff themselves with tinned pineapple. Particularly not when their available sanitary arrangements are totally inadequate.

That evening all of Hurworth Place came down with the squirts. At first it was just a case of netty doors opening and closing briskly with a brief exchange such as "Ta very much" and "Is there any paper, hinny?" and "By, but it's a warm neet!" But the pace quickened, the cordiality dwindled and anxious neighbours came along the back lane, clacking backyard snecks, seeking relief.

Then the nightmare began to gather pace and the bairns got started, the little uns and the bigger bairns too. Then the bubbling started. Very soon there were tearful bairns squatting on flowered chamberpots in every yard, biting rag dolls, plucked out of bed, hoyed out of house and home for gassing their grannies. The flutes of flatulence began to play a lively jig in Hurworth Place that night.

Then the queues began at the netty doors, and like a shipyard buzzer the first thin wail of terror arose on the evening air when it became obvious to the sufferer that she wasn't going to be admitted before the terrible moment of truth arrived. Khaki drawers became the regimental badge of Hurworth Place.

Then panic burst like shrapnel. Men who had survived the butchery of Passchendaele unbroken begged for mercy. Helpless fists hammered on netty doors. Voices that at other times and places would have melted hearts of stone were unheeded. Desperate pleas filled the plaintive air, falling on deaf ears.

That summer eve was wild with voices imploring, beseeching, begging, threatening! Bairns sat bellowing on any leakproof container. Old wives ran from yard to yard like heedless chickens. Men with strained, set faces walked stiff-legged from Hurworth Place, lepers seeking sanctuary, crying silently, unclean, unclean!

It was Mrs. Rita Chamberlain who invented the portable netty, sitting every leaky Chamberlain mite upon a pineapple tin. Popular demand emptied the cart in minutes, yet the gentle dusky maidens smiled through every indignity.

Lecky Fergie? I viewed the whole tragedy from our kitchen window betweenwhiles writing a letter to Shirley Temple thanking her for the pineapple treat while Our Mam and Our Dad, Granny and Auntie Bella ran wildly up and down the stairs cursing the very name of the deadly fruit.

"What's going on?" I asked and wished I hadn't when I saw my father's face. What was going on was that my Grandfather was besieged in the netty and refusing to come out to accept a free transfer to the Jubilee biscuit tin to ease Our Mam and Auntie Bella's sufferings. Our Dad was about to prise the hinges off the netty door with the kitchen poker. That's what was going on. Just an everyday occurrence in the boisterous saga of the Fergies of Hurworth Place.

The terror rose to its absolute crescendo at about eleven that night when all the lucky bairns and even luckier adults were sitting on chamberpots, pineapple tins, buckets and pails, souvenir biscuit tins and even a pot from which an indignant aspidistra had been evicted.

Those sufferers who were so fortunate as to be in possession of a netty were falling asleep from exhaustion; a state of collapse brought on not only by the terribly dehydrating diarrhoea, but also by the sheer physical struggle to escape eviction. Not to be pulled out into the yard in a state of dishabille as happened to old Jackie Robson who politely opened the door to explain his position. Only to find his new position was sitting on the bin with his trousers down about his ankles.

By dawn it was all over. There were some to whom the ultimate disgrace was something never to be discussed even with their nearest and dearest, but the further that ghastly night receded over the years the more it became the subject of fond laughter.

Uncle Freddie? Well, this is the true story of how he became the Pineapple King of Jarrow. Yet despite popular demand for him to decorate a lamp post he was mysteriously absent. He was found two days later at Davidson's farm where he had been haymaking, bronzed and fit, while the rest of Hurworth Place was weak, wobbly and white.

The charity vouchers in my beer crate? When all the fuss and fury died down I gave them to Our Mam who shared them with Auntie Bella. A sort of compensation fund, y'might say.

Lecky? Oh, I was all right. But that comes of doing what Uncle Freddie said a good soldier should do: never ever letting go of my old tin hat.

For the Honour of the Family

When I was a child living in Hurworth Place, we lived so close together, the terrace might have been a ship and the Placers the crew of our vessel. As we shared the daily round, the common task, we were more aware of our neighbours than perhaps, people today of the noisy, anonymous world about them. We shared laughter and tears, bread and hunger, happiness and sorrow, wounds and pain, birth, death, influenza and impetigo.

When I was but a round-eyed fledgling there was a lark sang on the Place and her name was Elsie Murphy. She must've been thirteen and I only two when first we met. I was sitting on our front step when this blue-eyed, raven-haired girl stopped to scoop ice cream from her ha'penny cornet and offer her thumb to my mouth. We were generous not only with our sorrows and successes, but our germane germs too. There and then, to the scent of vanilla ice cream, I fell in love with Elsie Murphy and often she would beg me from my mother to take to the park to be played with as girls did in those days: a sort of surrogate motherhood. Elsie had the voice of an angel and she sang the ballads her mother taught her. When today I hear an Irish lark I'm sitting again on the grass of the West Park loving Elsie and watching her make a daisy chain to loop about my neck. She sang as easily and naturally as other people breathed. My mother would take a break from her possing to listen to Elsie singing from yards away. In all the yards and kitchens of the Place women must've paused at their work to listen to that sweet voice.

The day Elsie stopped singing was the day she started to scream. Late one afternoon when our busy crew were scrubbing down decks and white sails blossomed in the sunlit lane Elsie Murphy began to scream. She screamed for an hour and cried until the sun set and there was no corner of the Place where one could escape the sadness of that voice. Nothing was explained to me, but Elsie never sang again and within a twelvemonth she was dead. Consumption was probably the primary cause, but years later Uncle Freddie told me my first love died of a broken heart. The day John Flynn came to ask permission to become engaged her parents became aware John was Elsie's cousin.

The poet says there is music in the midst of desolation, but that's not true. It's a lie. In the midst of desolation there is only pain and loneliness, pain that wounds and loneliness that kills. In the end love betrays us all. As I betrayed Granny Fergie for the sake of one of Ali Jamjar's Lucky Bags.

Ali Jamjar was the ragabone man who paraded the streets of Jarrow with his horse and cart, blowing a bugle very badly, but loud enough to wake the dead. Ali was a big black man, wrapped up in somebody's old curtains. On his head this prime player in the street theatre of old Jarrow wore a sultan's turban with a great rubystone pinned to the brow. His horse was Bucephalus who carried Alexander to the gates of India and was now content to walk the cobbled streets of Jarrow behind the black prince, Ali Jamjar.

The ragabone man would set up shop in the lane and blast the neighbourhood through a battered megaphone, his voice bouncing off the walls, like an artillery barrage, waking not only the dead, but the unfortunates abed like my father who worked the nightshift.
"Haway, lads and lasses!" Ali would boom, "For ya Mam's auld woollies I'll give yi a big balloon. For copper and lead, cash in hand. Nee questions asked. How's about a geet big toffee apple for your Da's auld boots? Gan on! I'll give ya Granda time to gerris kecks on if yi want to sell ya Granny's bed. Bring iss a decent coat, lads and lasses and yi'll have one of Ali Jamjar's Lucky Bags! Best in arl Jarrer!"

The height of social success was the possession of one of Ali's Lucky Bags. Only very best friends would be invited into your backyard for the Official Opening of the Bag. What was in the Bag? In one of Ali's Lucky Bags you'd always find Dolly's Mixture or BigGob lollies, a whistle or a clicky bug, wax lips or billy-stampers, rings with heart-shaped jewels, real jewels mind, water-squirters, chewing gum or Spanish boot laces, football pictures, candy Woodbines, film star pictures and the ones from the wireless, scented cachous to hide your breath and liquorice torpedoes you could lick and paint your lips red with if you were a lass. If you were a lad you could paint your face like a Red Indian and make the lasses run away. That's what you'd find in one of Ali's Lucky Bags. But even more important was the fact that in every thousandth Bag there was a pound note. There had to be, by law.

I only once had one of Ali's Lucky Bags. I didn't have it long. I didn't even get to open it. Was it the thousandth Bag with the pound note by law, d'y'think? Uncle Freddie wouldn't let me keep it. He said it was stolen property.
The child within me cringes when I remember those words and recollect his face. Old wounds reopen at the very whisper of remembrance. It is the wrongs we never can put right that linger longest. Time steals away the remedy.
I stole my Granny's only coat and swapped it for a Lucky Bag. There, I've said it and that's what I did. I'm still ashamed. Which makes this story so hard to write. I hear the childish voice, the tumbling excuses. She didn't want her coat. She said she didn't. It hung behind the kitchen door forever. She never wore it. She always wore her shawl. When our Mam would say to her, "Wear your coat, you'll catch your death of cold, Mam," Granny would say, "I'll only be foisted, Mary," and wrap her shawl tighter.
I stole my Granny's coat and betrayed the love of an old woman who would gladly have died for me. The cowardly child within me protests his innocence and blames Norman Richardson. It was all his fault. He made me do it. How could he make you do it? He had a Lucky Bag. I never had a Lucky Bag. He wouldn't let me in his yard. He let everybody in but me.

I stood outside Norman Richardson's bolted backyard door and pleaded with him through the cracks.
"When I get a Lucky Bag I'll let you in our yard, Norman Richardson," I cried, "You know I would."
"You'll never have a Lucky Bag, Leckie Fergie!" cried my tormentor, safe within his castle walls.
"Lerris in, eh?" I pleaded, "Your Mam would lerris in. She says I'm a real tonic. A laugh a minute. She wouldn't want me left out!"
Norman's righteous voice oozed through the door reducing me to desperation.
"Yes, she would!" he taunted me, "She only let me have the Lucky Bag on condition I wouldn't let you in. She said, don't you dare let that Lecky Fergie in our yard!"
"You're a liar! She'd never say that!" I cried, but the only reply was sniggering laughter.
"Right!" I threatened, "I'm going round your front door to tell your Mam. Then you'll be forrit!"
But it was an empty threat. It was all my own fault anyway. I was supposed to

be Norman's best friend, but it wasn't a true friendship. What I wanted was his encyclopaedias, THE CHILDREN'S ENCYCLOPAEDIA, Volumes I – XII. Mrs. Richardson was desperate for her darling son to have a playmate at any cost so her generosity with Little Gem biscuits and gallons of Robinson's Barley Water did little to discourage me from knocking on her front door, but it was access to the Encyclopaedias that I craved. There was a price to pay. His mother would scrub my hands and face with a soapy flannel before I was allowed to touch the precious Encyclopaedias. A small penance to pay for admission to the world of knowledge hidden in those musty pages.

However since my mother brought me my own Encyclopaedias from Mrs. Blenkinsop's I had rather neglected Norman. I did miss the Little Gems and Robinson's Barley Water, but I didn't have to put up with that smelly flannel any more. That's why he wouldn't let me into his yard to share the Lucky Bag with him. So, within the convoluted logic of childhood, Norman Richardson was to blame for me stealing Granny's coat.

The day my mother brought home the Encyclopaedias was the golden hour of my childhood. I was reading by our kitchen window and Granny Fergie was dozing in her chair when I heard my mother and Auntie Bella's voices in the yard. My mother called for me and I ran downstairs to the yard.
"Yes, our Mam?"
My mother said, "If you think we're carting these up the stairs you've got another think coming."
My mother looked tired, but Auntie Bella was smiling. Between them stood the big laundry basket filled with linen. I came forward hesitantly.
"What've you got?" I asked, "Is it something for me?"
Auntie Bella lifted a great armful of linen. I gasped when I saw what filled the basket.
"The Children's Encyclopaedia! Volumes One to Twelve! Oh, our Mam!"
I found I couldn't breathe. A great feeling of joy and love and guilt swept over me.
"Well?" my mother asked, "Don't yi want them?"
I looked at her with eyes like Chinese saucers.
"For me, our Mam? Are they really and truly for me?"
Auntie Bella gave me a poke to restart my heart, saying, "You're the daftie that sets fire to the chimley flying letters up to Santa for Encyclopaedias. Wi've come to the right house, haven't we?"
"Yes, Auntie Bella, but…for me?"
"Who else would your Mam be dragging this ton weight home for?"

I was so happy and yet so near to tears. My cup did truly runneth over with joy. Yet the best I could do was stare speechless at this treasure trove in the laundry basket and from there to my mother's expectant face.
"Well?" my mother said, "Say something, daftie. Wi've dragged them far enough."
"All the way from Mrs. Blenkinsop's at Tyne Dock," Auntie Bella reproved me, "I told your Mam it was too much for her, but, no, she wouldn't listen."
"I mean," said my mother, "if they're the wrong ones wi'll take them back."
"No, no!" I cried, "Thank you, our Mam. Thank you very much."

I fell to my knees in adoration. To worship the books. I know now I should have hugged and kissed my mother. I should've shouted that I loved her. I should have let my joy explode that she saw so clearly to the heart of the matter. That she should know exactly what I wanted, what I needed. I know now what I should have done, but I thought there was plenty of time. I thought mothers were forever. Not for such a little time.
"Get up, yi daftie!" she cried, "No wonder your knees are like the fire grate. And no more questions. In future find your own answers."
"I won't ever ask anything again," I assured her, "How did yi get them? They must've cost a lot of money."
Auntie Bella wanted to explain how Mrs. Blenkinsop had put out the Encyclopaedias for the binman to take away, but when my mother asked to have them for her son, the greedy woman sold them to her. My mother paid the price with her poss stick and needle to set me free.
All Auntie Bella said was, "Your Mam's an angel. And a fool. To let that woman take advantage of you, Mary!"
My mother looked at her sharply and said, "Don't spoil the bairn's pleasure, Bella," and to me, "Are you listening to me?"
"Yes, our Mam," I answered dutifully.
"Mrs. Blenkinsop's Reggie has done very well for himself," my mother explained, "He's in the Town Hall. And that's all because of these Encyclopaedias. Mrs. Blenkinsop wanted you to have them. So you could do as well for yourself as her Reggie."
"How generous of Mrs. Blenkinsop!" I cried, "Perhaps one day I can repay her kindness. She must be the kindest, sweetest lady in all Tyne Dock."
"Well," said my mother, "I wouldn't go so far as to say that."
"Well, I would!" I responded boldly, "I shall always think of her as my Fairy Godmother."
Auntie Bella laughed and my mother glared at her.
"If you say a word, Bella," warned my mother.

"Fairy Godmother's not the word I would use," Auntie Bella said.
"What word would you use?" I enquired brightly.
Auntie Bella ignored my mother's dragon-face to say, "Use your Encyclopaedias. I suggest yi start looking under B."
"Bella!" warned my mother, and turned on me, "Are you gona shift these books or not? I'd like ti put me feet up afore they fall off."
"You and Auntie Bella go up," I suggested, "I'll manage the books. Granny's made a pot of tea. She knew yi were coming. She always does."
They turned into our bottom door and I called after them, "And I'll find the right word for Mrs. Blenkinsop!"
Auntie Bella laughed and my mother, oddly, laughed too. After all, they were loving sisters.
Thus it was that I nourished in my heart the image of my Lady Bountiful, Mrs. Arthur Blenkinsop of 17, Jesmond Terrace, Tyne Dock, and commended her to Jesus every night in my prayers. Top of the list. Gentle Jesus, meek and mild look upon Mrs. Blenkinsop...Thus it was that this foolish child, shut out from the false paradise of Norman Richardson's back yard, crept like a thief in the night to steal Granny Fergie's coat from the back of our kitchen door.

Ali Jamjar's cart still stood in the lane as Ali sorted his newest acquisitions. I ran towards him, waving the coat.
"Wait for iss, Mr. Jamjar," I cried, "I've got yi something."
Bucephalus turned his head to watch my frantic approach.
"Don't kill yourself, son," said Ali, "Bucie isn't that keen on shifting yet. I go when he goes."
I arrived breathless at the cart, a stitch in my side and a pain in my heart.
I gasped out, "I want one of your Lucky Bags, please."
"All the bairns do, son," Ali reassured me, "They all want one of Ali's Lucky Bags. What've yi got then? If it's woollens I've some cracking balloons."
I clutched Granny's coat to me.
"It's a coat, Mr. Jamjar. I want a Lucky Bag for this coat. It's well worth it."
I couldn't quite bring myself to let go of Granny's coat.
The big black man said, "Aye, well, are yi gonna let iss have a look at it?"
I surrendered the coat and my honour, gazing awesomely up at the rubystone shining like a third eye.
"It's a woman's coat," said Ali.
"It's me Granny's," I said, and inspired, "She's getting a new coat for Christmas."
"It's not Christmas yet," said Ali, reasonably, "What's she gonna do 'til then?"
"She doesn't go out a lot, "I lied, "She's got veins."

Ali looked at me sternly, "You're sure your Granny knows you've got her coat?"
"Yes. She wants me to have a Lucky Bag."
"What's your name?"
"Lecky Fergie."
"Who's your granny?"
"Granny Fergie. She and Grandad live with us."
"Fair enough," said Ali and reached into the cart, "Here ya, son. Hope it's a lucky bag for you."
As soon as Ali Jamjar put the Bag into my hand I knew I'd betrayed the honour of the family. Bucephalus lost patience and started to move off and Ali climbed onto the cart. Even as I changed my mind the cart vanished round the lane end. I wanted to cry out to him to stop, to take the Lucky Bag and give me back the coat, but my tongue was frozen. When the ragabone cart vanished there was silence in the lane. There was no envious crowd clamouring for me to open the Bag and share the spoils. There was no delicious anticipation of what the Bag might contain. There was only a deep self-loathing and the stirring of fear of what my father would do when he found out I was a thief. I was drowning in self-disgust, with the unopened Lucky Bag in my hand, when Uncle Freddie came out of their kitchen door.
"What's up, old sausage?" he asked, "Yi look like yi've lost a quid and found a tanner."
He smiled and I struggled against tears to confess to him, "Uncle Freddie, I gave Granny's coat to Ali Jamjar."
He digested this information and said, calmly, "You took her coat from the kitchen door?"
I couldn't trust myself to speak. I nodded miserably.
"You didn't ask her?"
"No," I said and hung my head. I wanted him to be angry
He was silent for a moment and then said, "Why would you do that, old sausage?"
"I wanted a Lucky Bag," I explained, "Norman Richardson's got one. Why shouldn't I have a Lucky Bag?"
He pointed to my hand, and said, "Well, you've got one."
I offered him the Bag, crying, "I haven't opened it. I don't want it. Can you get Granny's coat back for me?"
"Which way did Ali go?" asked Uncle Freddie.
I pointed and he seized my arm.
"Come on, run for ya life! We might catch him yet!"

We ran like the wind, hearing in the distance the faint echo of the bugle. Even

as we ran a deep sense of relief began to steal through me because Uncle Freddie was there, a sense of relief mingled with a deep and lasting shame. Then we turned the corner into Bedeburn Road back lane. There stood the cart. Ali was doing business. We stood panting, recovering our breath.
"Uncle Freddie," I asked, "Why aren't you angry with me?"
"Who says I'm not?" he answered, and then, "I woulda been if you'd opened that Bag."

It wasn't as simple a transaction as I'd hoped, returning the Lucky Bag to Ali Jamjar.
"Be reasonable, man," said Ali to Uncle Freddie, "If I gave stuff back every time a bairn changed their mind."
"The lad had no right to give it ti yi," Uncle Freddie responded.
"Well, he took the Lucky Bag right enough," Ali countered.
Uncle Freddie said, "Look, man, he's never even opened it."
"I've never even opened it, Mr. Jamjar," I cried, in ragged chorus.
"Sorry, son," said Ali Jamjar, "But I've a crust and scrape to make. Rules is rules. So, if your Uncle lets go of the horse."
"I'm not letting yi go without I have the old woman's coat," Uncle Freddie announced.
Ali Jamjar laughed.
"Don't be daft, man," he suggested, "Let go the horse."
"Not afore I have the coat," declared my resolute Uncle, "That's the only coat the old woman's got."
"All right," said Ali Jamjar, "Yi can have it."
"Oh, thank you, Mr. Jamjar!" I cried.
"I'll sell it to yi," said the ragabone man.
Uncle Freddie said, indignantly, "I wouldn't buy what's ours by right."
"Then I've no time to argue," Ali Jamjar concluded, "Let go the horse."
"Right," said Uncle Freddie, "If there's no way round it, I'll fight yi forrit. Lecky, hold me coat. Your Auntie Bella'll go mad if I get his blood on it."
Ali Jamjar stood bemused as my uncle stripped off his jacket and squared up.
"Uncle Freddie," I cried, "Mr. Jamjar's twice as big as you!"
Ali Jamjar laughed, a deep rumbling volcano of a laugh.
"Listen to the bairn, man, " he said, "Think on the bairn."
Freddie said, "He'll be away home. Afore I knock yi down."
Ali Jamjar laughed his disbelief.
"Man, I have no quarrel with yi," said Ali Jamjar.
"Will yi give the old woman back her coat?"
"I cannot," said Ali Jamjar, "Business is business."

"Then put up your dukes!" cried Uncle Freddie, dancing like a ferret on a hot copper. Ali Jamjar stared at him in amazement.

"You're serious, aren't yi, yi daft begger?" cried Ali Jamjar.

"Fight me for the coat!" cried Uncle Freddie, "Or you're not the man I took yi for!"

Ali Jamjar shook his head in wonder at the dancing dervish who flourished knotted fists inches from his nose.

"Yi've no choice!" cried Uncle Freddie.

"Right," said Ali Jamjar, reluctantly, "I must be as daft as you. But I cannot fight yi now. I've got me round to finish."

"When then?" Uncle Freddie demanded.

"Sunday morning?" suggested Ali Jamjar, "Ten o'clock suit yi? Anywhere particular?"

"Our back lane," Uncle Freddie said, "Hurworth Place?"

"You're sure yi want to do this?"

"I'll be there. Will you?" Freddie demanded.

"Oh, I'll be there. I like a good laugh," said Ali genially, and turning to me, he said, "Yi can keep the Lucky Bag, son."

I said, "I don't want it, Mr. Jamjar."

Ali accepted the Bag from me, and peered at the top corner.

"Would you believe it?" he said.

"What?"

"Bag number one thousand. Sure yi don't want it?"

His eyes were kindly, his mouth generous; he offered the bag to me in good fellowship.

"I'm sorry, Mr. Jamjar," I said, sadly, "I can't take it. It's not mine."

This answer seemed to satisfy him. He tossed the Bag onto the cart.

"Cheer up, son, we all make mistakes," he said and climbed on to the cart. He whistled at Bucephalus who ambled away shaking his head in amazement at the antics of the Yahoos.

As we walked home in a subdued silence, I plucked up courage to speak to Uncle Freddie.

"I'm sorry," I said, "I'm very sorry."

To my surprise he smiled and said, "Good lad! Sorry's sometimes the hardest word to say, but it's a wonderful ointment for sore places."

We walked on and I said, "Our Dad says a good big 'un will always beat a good little 'un."

"Does he now? Well, mebbes so, but it's not always the size of the man in the fight that matters," responded my pugnacious Uncle, "It's the size of the fight in the man that counts."

We walked in silence as I tried to work that one out.

The fight between Ali Jamjar and Freddie Dean turned into one of the great sporting occasions of the year in Jarrow as the rumour circulated that Ali Jamjar was really Jack Johnson, Heavyweight Champion of the World, exiled from Yankeeland for marrying a lass without looking at the colour of her skin first. As might have been expected the Prime Minister, Stanley Baldwin, complete with pipe, turned up to referee the bout and Edward, Prince of Wales, complete with Mrs. Simpson, was seen at Mrs. Maconochie's kitchen window, declaring something must be done. Precisely what or to whom nobody could remember.

All the upstairs kitchen windows were crowded, the back lane walls thronged with spectators, the lane crowded and the ring marked out with washtubs and wash lines. The Auld Pollis was there, supposedly to control the crowd, but really to put down the pollises' bets on Ali and see the bookies didn't skedaddle without paying up. Rea's ice-cream barrow did a roaring trade and Ossie Mandias, the Hebburn bookie, complete with running shoes, took in every spare penny while Freddie gave away at least a foot in height and three or four stone in musculature. The only people missing from the festive scene were Our Dad who was fed two pennorth of laudanum from Rose's the Chemist to keep him from joining in and Auntie Bella who wanted nothing to do with the whole disgraceful spectacle.

In the royal box of our kitchen window, on our kitchen chairs, sat our butcher, Mr. MacAtominey and his wife and daughter, the beautiful Charlotte. One day I would fall in love with Charlotte MacAtominey and love her all my life, but today I was more interested in pugilism than pulchritude. Mr. MacAtominey had presented my mother with a complimentary pound of MacAtominey's Family Sausage and a quarter pound of sweetbreads, which was her especial weakness, for the privilege of sitting at our kitchen window to see Uncle Freddie fight Jack Johnson for the Heavyweight Championship of the World.

There was a roar like the winter surf on Shields beach as Ali Jamjar came down the lane, dressed in his best velvet curtains, head and shoulders and most of his chest above the crowd, but there was an even greater row like all the yard hooters sounding off together when Bella's kitchen door opened and Uncle Freddie, the great white hope, in his off-white bodyshirt and linings emerged, followed by his seconds, Granny and Grandad Fergie.

The crowd fell silent as Stanley Baldwin called both men to the centre of the ring and explained to them the agreement he had reached with the American Government on the terms which would extinguish the British debt of £978,000,000 in sixty-two years at three per cent for the first ten years and three and a half per cent thereafter. Both men were deeply impressed by his lucid summation and agreed not to punch each other in the goolies.

When the spoon rattled on the poss tub, Uncle Freddie was first out of his corner, taking the fight to his opponent, rattling his ribs and, jumping like a Jack-in-the-box, drawing claret from Ali's nose. But as fast on his feet as he was, our dancing dervish, my brave uncle was caught out with a staggerer that bounced him off the Auld Pollis and started a cut above his left eye. However, by the end of the third round Ali Jamjar knew he was in a real fight and had his work cut out protecting a midriff that resembled a purple weskit.

Granny and Grandad performed miracles with vinegar and the family washclout in our hero's corner, but by the end of the sixth round it was obvious our gallant battler was beginning to show more than a little wear and tear. It was, you might say, a matter of a penguin pecking at a walrus. By the end of the eighth round the crowd had fallen silent. Both men were tired, Freddie exhausted, both bleeding freely from cuts, but while both Freddie's eyes were closing on the world, Ali could still see enough through his left eye to hit the mark.

When the spoon rattled for the ninth round, Freddie was wobbling on his pins as Ali came from his corner. Freddie punched blindly at the air through closing eyes, sensing his opponent's approach. Ali accepted the punches on his palms and came to put an arm round Freddie in comradeship as much as for support.
"Whoa, hang on, little man! I've had enough," said Ali, "You're a grand fighter and a bonny lad. I'm proud to take a beating from yi."
So saying, he took Freddie's right wrist and raised his hand to the sky.
"Ladies and gentlemen, the winner!" Ali Jamjar cried, "Show your respect for the champion, if you please!"

The applause was thunderous for both men despite the bookies having a field day. Ossie Mandias strolled away with his money bag hanging like a hernia. Freddie went gratefully to sit on his washtub and, surprise, surprise, Bella came out from the kitchen with a bowl of clean water to bathe his battered face tenderly. So she must've been watching the fight though she always denied it. Ali kissed Granny Fergie and restored her coat. My grandfather shook his hand warmly and Ali winced. My mother hesitated and then took a wet cloth to wash Ali's bloodied face and dab at the cut above his eyebrow. At the worst of times it was also the best of times. The honour of the family was upheld.

From that day onward, to my amazement, my Uncle Freddie and Ali Jamjar became fast friends. One day as we sat in companionable silence, enjoying the radiant warmth of the kitchen fire, coals crumbling in the grate, toasting stale bread, [ah, toast, the utter luxury of toast!] with the rain beating on the kitchen window pane, warm, loved and wanted, I asked him how this could be: that friendship should grow out of pain.

"Friendship," said my Uncle Freddie, "is measured by adversity."
He flourished the bread impaled upon the toasting fork as Arthur lofted Excalibur.
"How'd'y'mean?" I asked from my perch upon the fender. I could hear his knees protest as he knelt to engage the kitchen fire in a toasting joust. He was, after all, the toast of Hurworth Place, undisputed champion of my world.
"When there's nowt in the house," said my dear Uncle, cheeks glowing, "the cat'll walk out on yi. But the dog'll stay and starve with yi. Measure your friendships by that mark. Adversity."
"Uncle Freddie?" I asked.
"Yes, old sausage?"
"You're burning me toast."
"My toast," he corrected me, "I favour a spot of charcoal. Tip-top for the digestion."

My mother, Mary Ferguson and her sister Bella Dean [with help from Granny Fergie] kept the families' heads above water by taking in other folks' washing and cleaning other women's houses; a great deal of labour for very little reward, scrubbing, polishing, dusting, washing, ironing, repairing underwear, shirts and linen. I wasn't aware at the time that my mother who suffered from bronchial asthma was dying because of the endless toil she endured without complaint.

On a particular morning when the women were hardpressed, I begged my mother to be allowed to help her carry Mrs. Blenkinsop's washing back to the grand house in Tyne Dock. I thought to cement my friendship with this wonderful woman who had so kindly set me on the road to a pensionable job in the Town Hall by her gift of the Encyclopaedias. Perhaps her Reggie and I would work side by side, expanding the circle of friendship wider yet? Reluctantly she agreed but strung so many warnings about behaviour round my neck I nearly fell off the tram seat.
"Can't yi just sit still like any other bairn?" my mother asked wearily.

"I thought we were gona run over that pigeon," I explained.
"The pigeon can look after himself," she said, "which is more than I can say for you."
She examined me yet again, fastening down an errant lock of hair with spit and a not unkindly hand.
"Just be on your best behaviour," she warned, trying as she did unsuccessfully all her life to flatten my ears against my head, reaching, absently, as she did so for her collar where had we been at home she would've had a fearsome array of pins with which to fasten my aural appendages to my cranium.
"Our Mam!" I cried, "I am on my best behaviour. I'm being as good as gold."
She regarded me with suspicion based upon sad previous experience.
"Don't overdo it! Save it for Mrs. Blenkinsop's. Just sit still and let the driver worry about the pigeons."
We sat in silence for a moment until another arrow of anxiety struck her heart. She gave me the sharpest glance.
"What now, our Mam?" I cried. Surely she wasn't going to produce her pinking shears and abbreviate my protruding pink ears to placate Mrs. Blenkinsop? Not on the tram!
"Did yi go down the yard afore we came away?" she demanded.
"Yes," I cried indignantly, "You know I did! You saw me!"
"Two choruses?"
"Two choruses, honest," I replied.
To ensure no unsightly stains on nether garments and a bladder as dry as the Gobi desert my mother insisted all the males in the household should sing two choruses before buttoning up. There were neighbours and even passers-by in the lane who considered us a deeply-patriotic family. So indelible is my mother's mark on me that, even today, with increasing age and absentmindedness I may find myself standing at a public urinal belting out two choruses of the National Anthem. It's remarkable how quickly this clears any public lavatory.

The tram rumbled through the gloom of Tyne Dock Arches and slowed to stop at Tyne Dock Gate. When the kindly conductor had carried off the basket and the tram had sighed, clattered and departed for Shields Pier Head, my mother braced herself and we took our handles to trudge to the cliff of tall Victorian houses that constituted Jesmond Terrace. We set the basket down at the end of the terrace while my mother regained her breath which regained breath she immediately wasted on another lecture on behaviour.
"For both our sakes," said my mother sternly, "when we get to Mrs. Blenkinsop's, mind your peas and queues."
"Yes, our Mam, " I said obediently.

"Wipe your feet like a cavalry horse. Be a good soldier and don't speak until spoken to."
"No, our Mam."
"Or else I'll wish I hadn't let you help with the basket. I wouldn't have anyway. If I hadn't been pushed for time!" she sighed.
I said, "I wanted to come. I wanted to help you and I want to thank Mrs. Blenkinsop for giving me the Encyclopaedias. For all her kindness in helping me get a job in the Town Hall. I expect Reggie and I will become good chums."
Unexpectedly, my mother looked at me and shook her head sadly.
"Well, I hope she's not a disappointment to yi, Lecky," she pronounced, "Don't expect too much. Then yi won't be disappointed."
I reassured her.
"I don't expect anything. I've got all I want."
I really meant to say, I love you.
"Have yi, my son?" she said and smiled at me, "I wish we were all as easy pleased."
We picked up our burden and walked to Mrs. Blenkinsop's front door. It was a house that was higher than the trees. My mother pulled on the bell and far away as down the dingly dell I heard the echo of the chimes. It was the sort of house that made you whisper.
I whispered to my mother, "It's a very posh house, our Mam."
"Don't let me down," was her reply, "Chin up! Gob shut!"
When the door opened my first view of Mrs. Blenkinsop was disappointing. She was a sour-faced woman with an enormous bosom, tightly curled ginger hair and the biggest teeth I had ever seen other than the parrot fish in the Encyclopaedia. She wore a severe blouse and a tweed skirt. Her face held not a hint of kindliness. If I had been older or more knowing I would've recognised the aura of greed.
"I'd given yi up," complained Mrs. Blenkinsop, "I've been expecting you a good half-hour since."
My mother spoke placatingly.
"I'm sorry ti put yi out, Mrs. Blenkinsop," said my mother, "It took a wee while longer this morning. My youngest give me a hand with the basket."
"Meanwhile I'm standing waiting on yi," said Mrs. Blenkinsop.
"I'm sorry," said my mother. When Adam delve and Eve span, who was then the gentleman?
"So you ought to be," sniffed Mrs. Blenkinsop. She stood as if considering whether to admit us or not. My mother waited patiently, holding her handle of the basket.
"Well, I suppose he'll have to come in," Mrs. Blenkinsop decided finally.

My mother gave me a warning glance and we carried the basket through the hall and down the stairs into the kitchen. At a nod from Mrs. Blenkinsop we hefted the basket on to the kitchen table. The lady of the house then deigned to notice me.

"Who's this when it's at home?"

My mother suggested, "Say good morning to Mrs. Blenkinsop, Lecky."

"Good morning, Mrs. Blenkinsop," I declared brightly, "Thank you ever so much for letting me have the Encyclopaedias now your son's in the municipal buildings. I'm looking forward to joining him in due course. I expect we'll become good chums, Reggie and I."

"What's the boy on about?" enquired Mrs. Blenkinsop of my startled mother.

"Lecky!" she cried in dismay, but it was too late. The needle had been applied to the gramophone record and the shellac was revolving at 78 revolutions per minute.

"You're my benefactress," I explained, "That's the word for you. Auntie Bella couldn't think of the right one, but she knew it began with b."

My mother regarded me with the same expression she wore the day the pot of geraniums fell from the kitchen window sill and killed the rentman's dog.

"But I found the right word," I assured this awesomely austere lady who was regarding me with the very same expression the rentman wore standing at our bottom door with his recently expired canine in his arms, "Benefactress. It's from the Latin. Bene facta. Good deeds."

There was a long silence. I could hear my mother breathing.

Mrs. Blenkinsop said, "Are you sure the boy's compost mental? He doesn't sound right in the head to me."

My mother sprang to my defence.

"He's just trying to thank you, Mrs. Blenkinsop. For the Encyclopaedias. He's hardly put them down since he got them."

I hastened to assure the good lady that I wasn't bidding for intellectual supremacy.

"I'm afraid, " I said, "I may be something of a disappointment to you. Although I'm up to DECK to ELEC I haven't made any electricity yet. I need a better magnet and stronger elastic."

Mrs. Blenkinsop now assured of my idiocy turned her attention to the contents of the basket, remarking reprovingly, "He shouldn't even be thinking of elastic at his age. I hope he wiped his feet. That's what I'd like him to be thinking of."

"That's what he's been taught to do," said my mother and gave me a glance that might've boiled an egg at ten paces, "Is there any extra jobs? I'd be glad to do what needs doing."

Removing items from the basket and subjecting them to close scrutiny, Mrs. Blenkinsop sniffed and said, "I thought there were nine pillow cases?"
"Eight," my mother assured her employer, "I always write them down."
"Hmm," said Mrs. Blenkinsop, "We'll check the linen cupboard anyway."
"Any extra cleaning," my mother urged, "Anything at all that needs doing. With Christmas coming on."
Mrs. Blenkinsop was unmoved. There was not the wrinkle of a smile at the holy name of Christmas. Uncle Freddie was pushing a handcart through the wintry cold. Our Dad was helpless in his bed. We stood at the edge of the wilderness once again and wild beasts moved in the darkness.
"Anything that needs doing," my mother pleaded.
Mrs. Blenkinsop sorted snow-white linen into different piles on the kitchen table, but there was never a kind word for all the hours of conscientious craft and care.
"I see you haven't shifted that beetroot," commented Mrs. Blenkinsop.
"It's only a shadow," countered my mother, "Beetroot's not easy. I'll give it an extra soak next time. But yi have to be canny with the bleach."
"A spot of elbow grease wouldn't come amiss," said Mrs. Blenkinsop.
"I've turned the edges of that sheet," said my mother, "And there were three pillow cases that were the better for a stitch or two. I never do anything but my best."

At the time I thought simply that my mother was behaving very oddly. It was only years later when she was gone, when it was too late to express my love and admiration that she should endure such humiliations to keep me fed, clothed and housed that I understood her love for me. With my father laid low yet again with his amputation stump rubbed raw as rump steak working at the bakery bench and Freddie unable to find even casual labouring, the burden lay on the women.

"I never have anything but the best," countered Mrs. Blenkinsop, "The Captain wouldn't stand for it."
I saw the Captain in my mind's eye. Overflowing my mind's eye at six feet seven in his stocking feet, neatly darned by Granny Fergie. He had red hair and a beard flaming like the sunset.
"He'll be home to-night," mused Mrs. Blenkinsop, "For Christmas. We always have a lovely Christmas. It's very special to us. With him being away so much over the water."
I saw the Captain with the parrot on his shoulder and his great sea boots rising like tree trunks to his knees.

"Well then, " said Mrs. Blenkinsop, "Let's see what needs doing."
My mother brightened like the blacksmith's fire.
"I'll just slip me coat off then, shall I?" she suggested, "Lecky won't be any trouble. Specially if he has a book. He's a grand reader. We're all gona be proud of him one day."
She smiled at me with all the simplicity of her honest heart.
"Will we, indeed?" retorted Mrs. Blenkinsop, "I certainly don't want his dirty hands on Reggie's books."
"He's very careful with books," countered my mother.
"He shouldn't have come."
"I had no one else, Mrs. Blenkinsop. It takes two to manage the basket."
The two women looked at me.
"Are you listening to me, boy?" demanded Mrs. Blenkinsop.
"He's very shy with strangers," said my mother.
"I'm shy, but I'm listening, Mrs. Blenkinsop," I said, struggling to appear both shy and attentive in the same breath.
"There is a chair in the hallway," threatened this fearsome woman, bending towards me like a gooseneck crane, "Sit there until your mother's done her work. Don't you dare get down. Do you hear me?"
"Loud and clear, Mrs. Blenkinsop," I answered, shyly, attentively. Her breath smelled of dark-brown gravy. She had four metal teeth.
"Or else I shall have something to say!" she concluded.

I sat in the stiff-backed chair and stared at the elephant's foot that Captain Blenkinsop had cut off to stand umbrellas in. Somewhere in Africa a bad-tempered elephant was limping along much like my father, but with three legs not one. There was much my father had in common with that elephant. The silence was broken only by the whisper of my mother's footsteps somewhere upstairs. Mrs. Blenkinsop had vanished into thick air. There was nothing for me to do once I had counted the floor tiles twice. I listened to the ticking of a clock. I swung my legs and creaked the chair. Nothing happened. The dust of centuries fell slowly making more work for my mother while I creaked and swung. Encouraged by the melodic chiming of the clock I began to sing quietly to myself.
"Oh, the moon shines bright on Charlie Chaplin, " I warbled, "His boots are crackin' For want of blackin'."
My mother appeared silently on the landing to shake a hand brush at me and whisper fiercely, "What're you up to?"
"Only singing," I whispered, adding defiantly, "They can't shoot you forrit!"
"You don't know Mrs. Blenkinsop," my mother returned.

"Are you nearly finished?" I asked in a hoarse whisper.
"No," sighed my mother, "Not nearly. Yi'll have to be patient."
"I've got nothing to do!"
"Well, I have!" hissed my mother, "Don't sing!" and vanished.
Defiantly I sang, "And his baggy old trousers they'll need patching Before they send him to the Dardanelles."
My mother reappeared to whisper hoarsely, "Don't come crying to me if she bites your head off!"
I remembered the metal teeth and fell silent. My mother vanished and dark clouds of boredom settled over the hallway as the sun retreated from shattering the stained glass of the inner door to rainbows.

On a pedestal in the hall was a statue of a boy holding a trio of cherries above his mouth in a gay gesture: apparently frozen in the very act of dropping the glistening fruit into his smiling gob. I put one foot on the floor and when no one rushed to bite my head off, I lowered the other cautiously to the polished tiles. It seemed only reasonable to avoid blood poisoning by stretching my legs to rid them of cramp. Even Mrs. Blenkinsop wouldn't want to find a dead boy cluttering up her hallway. As slowly as treacle escaping from the tin I crossed the hallway to examine this monument to the sculptor's art: Boy with Cherries. He was smiling cheerfully despite having his left big toe missing. Perhaps Mrs. Blenkinsop had bitten it off to encourage him to smile more cheerfully?

I was just reaching up to see if the cherries were real when Mrs. Blenkinsop shouted at me, "Get your paws away from there!"
When she shouted I jumped six feet in the air propelled by shock and the Boy with Cherries jumped too, hoisted by my delinquent hand. Unfortunately the Boy made a very poor landing, shattering into a thousand plaster pieces across the tiled floor of the hallway. His severed hand still clutched the cherries, but the mouth laughed no more.
"You little sod!" screamed Mrs. Blenkinsop and advanced upon me, metal teeth flashing.
"I'm sorry, Mrs. Blenkinsop!" I cried, "I didn't mean to. I really didn't. I'm sorry."
She loomed above me, incandescent with rage, and screamed, "You will be! I'll give you something you'll not forget!"
Mrs. Blenkinsop then hit me across the head with the vase she was holding. I suppose I was lucky she wasn't carrying a flat iron. As I fell to my knees with Canterbury bells ringing in my head I saw my mother yank Mrs. Blenkinsop away and disarm her. I saw her momentary hesitation as to whether to dash the

vase to the deck and then, thinking better of it, placed it on the hall table. She turned in a fury on Mrs. Blenkinsop, and demanded, "How dare you strike my son?"

"The little bugger broke my Boy!" retorted that dear lady.

My mother raged like the winter sea.

"Yi had no right ti hit him!"

"No right?" Mrs. Blenkinsop responded, "I had every right. If you cannot control him somebody has to!"

I thought for a moment my mother was going to hit Mrs. Blenkinsop. I staggered to my feet, Canterbury bells change-ringing Treble Bob in my head and my mother put her arm about me instead.

"Profuse apologies, Mrs. Blenkinsop!" I cried, "It was an unanticipated accident."

"The state of your bowels is not my concern!" the worthy lady cried, "You've destroyed my poor Boy!"

My mother, recovering herself, always calm in a crisis, said, "You've no one to blame but yourself."

"Me?" Mrs. Blenkinsop in tones worthy of any Italian prima donna, "Just how d'y'make that out?"

"I heard yi shout," said my mother, "Then the ornament fell. Yi frightened him. That's why it got broken."

"Never!" announced that unworthy lady, "It was in pieces when I got to him."

My mother looked at this overfed woman who lived in great luxury and security, in a wonderful house furnished with possessions far beyond our reach, even an indoor lavatory and a bath with brass taps and said, "You're a liar, Mrs. Blenkinsop."

"How dare you speak to me like that?" cried my mother's erstwhile best customer.

My mother said calmly, "If you'll pay me for the wash and the morning's work, we'll be on our way."

"Pay yi?" that ignoble woman sneered, "After what that little sod's done? I'll set your money against the damages."

Mrs. Blenkinsop marched to her front door and held it open.

"Now out! Out the pair of yi!"

My mother stood fast and said, reasonably, calmly, "Mrs. Blenkinsop, you owe me for the wash and the morning's work. I won't argue for the mending, but that's only reasonable."

"Reasonable? I know what's reasonable," crowed that contemptible creature, "If you're not gone in two minutes I'll have the pollis on yi! Then we'll see who's a liar!"

We knew from past experience who the police would believe and it wouldn't be the washerwoman and her son.
I announced, "I'm going to be sick, our Mam," and suited the action to the word.
"Out!" cried Mrs. Blenkinsop as I spewed diced carrots across the shining tiles, "Out!"
"By the way, I keep meaning to tell yi your house smells of cacca," my mother riposted as we quit the field with honour, "I mean, who'd have a lavvy in the house?"

Out on the pavement my mother upturned the wash basket and sat me on it.
"Take deep breaths and think of something nice," she said and blew my nose on her clean pinny which she'd never have done if she hadn't been so distracted by the loss of her money and employment. My mother wasn't thinking nice thoughts to settle her stomach. Concussion hadn't been invented then so she didn't rush me to the doctor. She waited until I'd finished emptying my digestive tract down to the last piece of diced carrot and swede and then took me home on the tram.

Uncle Freddie came up to see me and examined the lump on my head.
"Well," he said, "you've got yourself a nest egg to fall back on."
"I did fall back on it," I told him, and sadly, "It hurt. I thought Mrs. Blenkinsop was going to be nice, but she wasn't. She was horrible to our Mam."
"Are yi fit?" he asked.
"As fit as Simmonds' donkey," I answered, "And he's been a better gluepot than he ever was a donkey."
"You're fit," he said, "Come on, let's go!"
"Where?"
"We'll give it another go to get your Mam's money. If you're willing to eat more humble pie?" my worthy uncle suggested.
I said, "I don't think Mrs. Blenkinsop'll give us anything to eat."
Uncle Freddie gave me an odd look and checked the temperature of my brow. Then we tiptoed onto the landing and down the stairs so as not to wake my father.

Mrs. Blenkinsop answered the door.
"Profuse apologies, Mrs. Blenkinsop!" I pleaded.
"You can profuse all you like!" she cried, her metal teeth glimmering the lamplight, "Yi'll not get a penny out of me!"
She tried to close the door, but Uncle Freddie's boot prevented her.

"Mrs. Blenkinsop, give iss a chance, will yi?" he suggested, "I'm Mary's brother in law. Her man's ill in bed. He has an ulcerated amputation stump. A little memento of the War-ti-end-all-wars.

Mrs. Blenkinsop sniffed. She had a very superior sniff.

"You're wasting your time here pleading for cripples. It's time they stood on their own two feet and earned their daily bread like decent folk."

Uncle Freddie was silent, but when he spoke it was through gritted teeth.

"You're a very lucky woman, Mrs. Blenkinsop."

"With me lovely Boy in fragments? I don't think so."

My uncle said, "You're lucky Davie Ferguson hasn't come round. He doesn't think he's a cripple."

"Oh, I see!" cried Mrs. Blenkinsop, "You're threatening a woman. I know your type."

My Uncle Freddie struggled to control his exasperation.

"Look, missus," he said, reasonably, "Mary's done a week's wash and mend for you. She cleaned house for you this morning. Have yi ever found fault with her work? For God's sake, woman, it's Christmas! Be fair! Does Christmas mean nowt ti you?"

Mrs. Blenkinsop vanished abruptly into thin air and for a moment hope shone in the frosty air. We gazed on one another with expectant eyes. Moved by Uncle's Freddie's pleading had she gone to hide sudden tears and find her purse? To confess to kindness and pay a little over the odds for the trouble and inconvenience?

She returned to flourish a familiar gay smile and a plaster hand clutching three imitation cherries under my bewildered uncle's nose, screeching, "D'y'see these?"

"I'd be blind not to," said my uncle, retreating before the dancing cherries.

With smug satisfaction the belle dame sans merci announced, "Yi'll not get a penny piece out of me! Now haddaway afore I have the pollis on yi!"

Then the head of the household appeared, chewing a mouthful of dinner. He solved the problem of his intransigent wife by pulling the lady into the house and shutting the passage door on her.

"Shut your gob for two minutes, woman," the gallant Captain suggested, "Or I'll shut it for yi."

He wasn't six feet tall, with a black eye patch, peg-leg and a parrot on his shoulder. He was the skipper of a weekly collier, five by five and as treacherous as a rattlesnake.

Uncle Freddie tried to explain the situation to him, but was cut off short by the gracious gentleman who spat something indigestible into the privet.

"Yi can see I'm at me dinner," said the collierman.

"You're lucky to have dinner," said Uncle Freddie, unruffled, "It'll be a poor Christmas for Mary's family 'less we sort this out."

"Yarra fancy man then?" the Captain enquired, unnecessarily offensive.

"No," Uncle Freddie answered, keeping his temper, "Not that it's owt of your business, I'm her sister's man."

"Where's her man then?"

"You'd be sorry if he came round," said Uncle Freddie shortly, "He's no diplomat."

"I'll tell yi what," said the boorish simian, housecleaning his foul mouth and scratching his neck to indicate deep thought, "I'm at me dinner as yi can see. Come back at...let's say nine and I'll see you're paid in full. I've never left a debt unpaid and never will."

"Fair enough," said Uncle Freddie, "Nine o'clock it is."

The passage door opened and the Captain's gracious lady who had heard every word, screeched, "He's too soft with yi! Yi wouldn't get a ha'penny out of me! Well, I won't have yi on me step. Round the back! Where yi belong. And it's not coming out of my purse! That the likes of them think they can...!"

"Shut your gob!" shouted her courteous counterpart to the sweetheart of his golden years, and to Uncle Freddie, "Paid in full. Nine o'clock. Round the back," and slammed the door.

As we walked away we could hear the woman screeching and the man's voice beating her down.

"And a Merry Christmas to you, too!" said Uncle Freddie.

In the frosty moonlight we walked the winter streets of Tyne Dock. There was no sense in marching to Jarrow and back again. In this unsought solitude I listened to my Uncle Freddie and began to perceive what it means to honour one's family, to be steadfast, to offer and receive love and respect.

"Yi fought Ali Jamjar," I said.

"Yi think fighting's the answer, d'yi?"

"Yi got the coat back."

"The coat wasn't worth a punch in the gob," he assured me, "Never mind two black eyes."

While I considered this statement my Uncle sang, "Two lovely black eyes. Oh, what a surprise! Twas only for telling a man he was wrong. Two lovely black eyes!" and laughed aloud at himself.

"Then why did you do it?"

Uncle Freddie said, "If you'd asked your Granny, she would've given you the coat. Right?"

"I suppose so. I never thought," I said.

"But then you would've had to refuse it," said he.
We stood together to count the stars and listened to the ships calling on the river.
"Why?" I said, puzzled.
"D'y'remember the time you told me, old sausage? " he said, "About Granny Fergie coming to meet you at school because it was raining. How she was soaking because she had your coat wrapped in her shawl to keep it dry."
"I couldn't understand how she hadn't worn her shawl," I ventured.
"Do you understand now?" he asked me gently.
I said, "Because she loves me?"
"There's hope for you yet," said my Uncle Freddie.
He spoke with the authority of love.

The last stroke of nine from Trinity Church clock was sounding when Uncle Freddie rapped on the backyard door of number seventeen. From the lane we heard the house door open and boots cross the yard to undo the bolt. The captain opened the door.
"I see ya prompt," he said, with a grisly smile, "I like that in a man."
"Nine yi said," answered Uncle Freddie, "It's a cold night so we'd like to be away if . ."
"In full," said this honourable man, "I pay all my debts in full."
To my astonishment he stepped aside, saying, "Right, lads, give him his due!"
Two bullyboys with cudgels stepped out into the back lane. The Captain shut the yard door and went into the house.
Uncle Freddie danced backwards to have the wall behind him, spat on his hands, squared up and said, "Haway then! Lecky! Stay out of this!"
The two grinning apes came at him from left and right. As Uncle Freddie moved to defend himself from the man on his left I kicked the other thug in the backside, but my intervention was pointless. The thug grabbed me and threw me aside. I fell striking my already tender skull on the back lane wall and the beating of my uncle began. I was struggling to get to my feet when out of nowhere came the Prince of Darkness who plucked the cudgel from one bullyboy's grasp and flattened him with a fist the size of a basalt boulder.
"Ali Jamjar!" I cried, "Oh, hoorah!"
The second bullyboy gaped open-mouthed at the giant in imperial robes, gaslight catching the rubystone in his turban, and then fled precipitately, his boots clattering over the cobbles like the applause of a single hand.
Ali Jamjar laughed out loud and stepped over our hero. He offered a hand to pull Uncle Freddie to his feet.
"All in one piece, Freddie?"

"Just about," admitted that battered gentleman, "I couldn't be more pleased to see yi."
"Is the lad all right?"
Freddie examined me for damage.
"I told you to stay out," he chided me.
Satisfied that I had only collected another nest egg to fall back on, he turned to Ali Jamjar.
"Where in Hades did you spring from, Ali?"
"Saw yi from the corner. Thought you might fancy a ride back to Jarrer."
"Much appreciated," said my Uncle Freddie, "Give iss two minutes and I'll be with yi."
As my uncle turned away, Ali Jamjar said, "If we're gonna keep spilling blood together, Freddie, best we're marrers, eh? Here, man, let's have your hand."
Uncle Freddie laughed and offered his hand gladly.
"Blood brothers, eh? Mostly mine if I'm not mistaken."
Ali and I watched while Uncle Freddie hammered on the Blenkinsops' back door. The kitchen door opened and a now familiar voice strained the wintry air.
"All right, all right, there's nee need to take the paint off! I only hope yi give him a good hiding. I'm not paying for half measures."
When the backyard door bolts were withdrawn it was a pleasure to see their faces.
My Uncle Freddie said, politely enough, "As I was saying when we were so rudely interrupted..."

On that Christmas Eve long years ago in the gaslit warmth of my mother's kitchen in Hurworth Place we sang carols beneath our homemade decorations; love's purse is never empty; and rejoiced to be together amongst the folk we loved and who loved us. The stars that wintry night shone as brightly as ever and the dark wilderness haunted by nameless beasts receded, never to return. Until next time.

The frosty stars shine as brightly as ever tonight. The Plough still points the homeward way. We can find our way to Jarrow any time we want. Home to where Christchurch steeple stands silver in the moonlight. But harder yet to find is that Jarrow where Palmer's cranes held up the sky and hammers sang on the river. Where I betrayed my Grandmother and disgraced Our Mam. Where my brave Uncle Freddie rescued Christmas and that elusive, slippery enigma called the Honour of the Family.

Another Woman's Child

Every time Granny Fergie wanted anything tested for goodness: green meat, milk-on-the-turn, stale bread, dodgy fish, soup bones, she would call my Grandfather, and demand he try this, taste that, and without the slightest demur the old man would take the bone or the ladle into his hand and obediently chew or swallow. Granny would stand with her head cocked to one side awaiting his verdict.

Grandad Fergie would purse his lips, savouring the bouquet, thoughtfully chewing until she would run out of patience and rap him with the ladle, saying, "Well, yi daft man? Is it or is it not?"

Sometimes he would insist on a further sampling before saying, "Tastes fine to me, Mary, but then I'm no judge." "Away with you, yi ninny," she would cry, threatening him with the ladle and away the bewildered man would wander, wondering why he'd been treated and threatened in the same instance. I would observe his departure, fearful that at any moment his legs would falter and he would fall dead to block the kitchen doorway, poisoned by my Granny.

On this occasion he had obligingly sampled a ham shank that Mr. MacAtominey the butcher had given Granny for free, thereby raising doubts in her mind of its fitness for human consumption.

What my Granny was unaware of was that Mr. MacAtominey was unconscionably fond of my mother and would call out, "Ah, the Rose of Hurworth Place!" whenever she entered his shop, an embarrassment she mostly avoided by sending me or Granny for our helping of MacAtominey's Best Mince or

MacAtominey's Family Sausage. That was how he talked. "Would it be the MacAtominey's enamel bath on four claw feet or the MacAtominey's zinc tub before the MacAtominey's kitchen fire?" is how one would imagine he addressed his Friday night's excursion in hygiene.

Whenever I went into his shop there was always an enquiry after my mother's health, an insistence on being remembered to her and an extra dollop of mince or sausage to tip the scales. Unless Mrs. Mac was in the shop when a covert wink would have to suffice.

"It does him no harm," Granny confided, shaking her head affectionately, guiltily, after Grandad's departing form, "It all comes away with the wind."

However, the last condition necessary for Granny Fergie to read the tea leaves had now been fulfilled. Grandad had left the house, gone to await the opening of the library where he and his fellow radicals might enjoy a peaceful browse through the morning papers regardless of the bustling world about them. So as not to indulge the undeserving poor in unnecessary luxury the men were required to stand to read the newspapers unlike the Holy Bible which was available in a seated posture. Was this a moral judgement on the perusing of the popular press?

Apparently Grandad Fergie's absence was essential to successful predictions. It was never clear to me whether the old man was particularly vulnerable to any passing spirit of wickedness or whether no respectable spirit would enter the premises while he was present.

I stood at the kitchen window to make sure the old man was away down the back lane. My Grandfather had a habit of settling himself to read the netty paper which comprised torn-up sheets of newspaper skewered, strung and hung on a nail in our little sanctuary. With some experience of jigsaws a determined reader could piece together an hour's entertainment with little difficulty.

Grandad Fergie was forbidden to take his reading specs into the netty and was forced by law to place them in the hole in the wall where a brick was missing by the netty door. If he was not closely watched his hand would sneak round the door and abstract his specs. He was not to be trusted, asserted Our Mam, nor any man for that matter. Descended from monkeys we might be, but the men haven't descended far enough, Auntie Bella would agree.

When he had emerged refreshed, retrieved his specs, blown his nose like a huntsman's horn and hopefully buttoned his fly, we could be pretty sure he was on his way to the Free Library.

The omens were propitious. Granny Fergie's penny was on the table, head upwards. This was either to prove our prosperity to any wandering spirit or to encourage it into thinking a large tip was available. Granny had her slippers on the wrong feet. This was to mislead any malicious spirit into believing it had entered the wrong house. It couldn't be Granny Fergie as this auld wife's feet were the wrong way round. Obviously a case of mistaken identity. The spirit would withdraw, taking his evil intentions with him, and we could all breathe again. One can't be too careful when tapping into eternity.

I was present. It is a wellknown fact that the young attract good fortune. We were ready to consult the occult. Solemnly Granny Fergie hushed me to silence with a finger to her lips. She took her cup, swirled the tea leaves and abruptly upended the cup in the saucer to trap fickle fortune. She began to skirl the cup in the saucer counting the turns.
"Un, deux, trois, ein, zwei, drei," she counted.
Granny picked up the cup and studied the pattern of leaves.
"Well? Wha'd'y'see?" I cried.
"It's a dark man," said Granny.
"That'll be Uncle Freddie," I said, craning my neck to see what only Granny Fergie could see.
"No," said Granny, shaking her head, brushing my ear with silver, "it's not Freddie. It's a stranger. Coming from a long way off."
I took the cup from her and peered at the erratic pattern of leaf fragments. I felt the stirring of excitement, a shiver of uncertainty.
"We don't know any strangers," I said, "Not coming from a long way off."
Granny took the cup from me and stared at the future.
"Is it good or bad?" I asked.
"I'm not sure," said the old soothsayer, adding soothingly, "But in the end it'll all come out all right. All will be well. In the end."

A shiver ran down into my boots. 'In the end' were three ominous words. In CAPTIVES OF THE CARIBBEAN that's what Jeremiah Blackett, the pirate captain, said to Ralph as he was lowered over the side for keelhauling. 'In the end you will obey!' Ralph'd finished holystoning the decks so they forced him to make a start on the keel. When he came back up his silk shirt was all torn and he'd lost one silver-buckled shoe, but he still had a watery smile for Arabella.

Of course, you haven't read CAPTIVES OF THE CARIBBEAN, have you? You should do. It'll bring your feet up onto the chair, especially the bit where the pirate captain is eaten by the sharks that he has encouraged to follow the ship by throwing the crew's pet rabbit overboard to be followed by Arabella who is rescued by Ralph even as her reticule is ravaged. But not the rabbit which so enrages Dirty Dick the cook that he pushes the captain overboard. Ralph loses his other shoe.

In that simpler, harsher, kinder, crueller world in which I began my pilgrimage through this vale of tears and laughter we were all big readers. We had no wireless and television was simply a dark cloud on the horizon, but we did have the Free Library and an insatiable appetite for cheap romances published by Chatter & Windows.

The happiest hours of my childhood were spent sitting on Auntie Bella's fender, breathing the sweet scent of fresh linen, reading aloud to the gentle rhythm of Auntie Bella ironing, with cooling irons being returned to the fire above my head. We took turns reading aloud to one another. When she tired of ironing Auntie Bella would sit down beside me, shoulder to shoulder, and we would leave the sad, rainy world of Jarrow behind us when we fled to the Caribbean. In case you're worried about the rabbit, when they're starving to death, Dirty Dick catches a shark and when they open it up the rabbit is still alive inside. That's the kind of story we liked. Stories that unlike life have happy endings.

So, with the ominous words of Sibylla lingering in my ears, I found my way downstairs to Auntie Bella to continue our joint reading of ANOTHER WOMAN'S CHILD.

The downstairs apartments in Hurworth Place were modest in area. From the backyard you stepped into a tiny scullery from which you stepped into the Room and beyond that was the bedroom. Beyond the bedroom was the street where we did most of our living anyway. If you entered this humble dwelling by the front door you passed through the bedroom into the Room. There was only one room serving every purpose. If you recognised a familiar nose or top-knot peeping from the bedclothes, you called, "Hello there, Mr. What's-it, all right now? Grand day, eh? Mind, we've been very lucky with the weather." If you were very unfortunate shocked faces in the Room would reveal you'd been conversing with the dead.

This domestic arrangement had other disadvantages. Leslie Gray's birthday tea was the shortest ever recorded in Jarrow. After ten minutes of the Duke of York marching his men past the bedfoot, we all, hostess, birthday boy and guests, fled screaming from an avenging fury arisen from the bedclothes. Mrs. Gray pleaded with her husband through the letterbox to be allowed back in to collect the sandwiches and cake, but a birthday tea on the pavement hasn't the same sparkle.

"Why've you stopped reading, Auntie Bella?" I asked.

Auntie Bella had lowered the book into her lap and sat staring at the ironing board. Then she stood up to poke the fire, causing the coals to collapse.

I persisted, saying "The summer sun was setting on Capel Fell when who came down the road? Who, Auntie Bella?"

It was our favourite pastime. Reading turn and turn about, Bella and me, blubbing at the sad bits, laughing at the happy ends. Sharing a book, as we so often did, transformed that simple Room into a wondrous treasure house.

"Who, Auntie Bella?"

My dear Auntie turned a tearful face upon me, laying aside the poker to dab at her eyes with a corner of her pinny.

"Oh, Lecky, pet," she said, "I don't think I can read it."

"It's not that Welsh word again, is it?" I asked, "Double-ella-gobba-lobba-go-go? Miss it out. You can say Swansea instead."

When I do shuffle off this mortal coil and if there is a Heaven and if I'm permitted past the Pearly Gates, I know Auntie Bella will be there, sitting on a golden fender, holding a book entitled TOGETHER AGAIN, waiting to share eternity with me.

"I don't think I can go on, pet," said Auntie Bella and fresh tears flooded her face.

"You've been reading ahead," I said accusingly, "When I went down the yard. You promised you wouldn't. You have, haven't you?"

We were both too easily brought to tears. Not by the hardships of Jarrow-in-Depression, but by the trials of such as pretty Jessie who had to cope with artful Archie, the squire's son. Auntie Bella's guilt was as plain to see as the tears on her face. A dreadful thought struck me.

"Has Dennis been thrown over the cliff again?" I asked, fearing the worst.

Auntie Bella pulled herself together to answer, "No. Dennis is all right. It's Eleanor," and dissolved into tears once more.

There was a Bad Girl in every romance we read. The Bad Girl always chased the hero and sometimes-always nearly caught him in her treacherous web. In ANOTHER WOMAN'S CHILD the hero was a handsome young cowherd called Dennis.

"What's happened?" I said, steeling myself for the worst.
Auntie Bella sat down beside me, and bravely, confidingly, said, "D'you remember in Chapter Eight, Lecky, when Eleanor went into the barn after Dennis?"
I nodded silently.
"And then we had the row of asterisks?"
My heart sank.
"I'd forgotten the asterisks!" I cried in horror.
Why Palmer's shipyard was shut and the best shipbuilders in the world were out of work was something I didn't understand. But asterisks I did understand. Asterisks make you pregnant.
I stared into her sad face wonderingly.
"But Dennis and Jessie were only married in Chapter Thirteen!" I cried.
Auntie Bella shook her head sagely, sadly.
"Unlucky for some. You read it, Lecky. I'm just too soft."
Soft? This ferrous fragmentiser who could lift our washtub over her head and not spill a drop. And make my Uncle Freddie toe the line. Well, sometimes anyway.
I picked up the book and began to read. I was very conscious of Auntie Bella's warm flank against me. I have never in my life anywhere felt happier, safer, more loved than in that simple kitchen. But fantasy was to us so real that I held the book with trembling hands, afraid of what I would discover on the page. I began to read aloud.

"'He is the soul of honour,' Jessie cried. Eleanor laughed triumphantly. 'Your fine Dennis is the father of another woman's child!' Poor Jessie, aghast at the swelling below Eleanor's tasteful riding habit, fell into a fearful swoon."

Isn't that just like happiness? You no sooner hold it in the palm of your hand than it melts away like a summer snowflake. I was shocked to the very core of my being. Dennis, decent Dennis, had betrayed sweet, simple Jessie, his childhood sweetheart!

"It can't be true, Auntie Bella," I cried in anguish, "Dennis loves Jessie. He said so. On page eighty seven. When he knelt in that cowpat in his best breeches."
Auntie Bella snorted her disbelief.
"Men are jellyfish, pet," said my redoubtable Auntie, "A flutter of a lace petticoat and they're away up the road without their tea."
"But Dennis is not like the Honourable Archie!" I insisted.
"Dishonourable Archie, more like!" Auntie Bella retorted and snorted all the louder.

I had to admit that the young squire spent an indecent amount of time in his dressing gown. Un-dressing gown more like. What honest man would wear a gown of Chinese silk after eight o'clock in the morning?

Auntie Bella pulled herself together, determined to make the best of things, drying her eyes on her pinny, accepting her disappointment. She had been rather attached to the name Dennis. There is a quality of gentility about the name that suggests tennis and French windows, cucumber sandwiches and sunny afternoons on the vicarage lawn, a proposal on the loveseat under the old apple tree and a solicitor for a husband, a spaniel named Charles and two darling children, Julian and Emma and a wind-up gramophone playing the latest hit.

"We should've cottoned on they were married too early. Only Chapter Thirteen. Marry in haste, repent at leisure," said Auntie Bella, resignedly.

"And those asterisks," I reminded her.

I'd forgotten that of all the risks true love runs asterisks are the worst.

"Perhaps it's a cushion?" I suggested hopefully.

Auntie Bella looked at me with true disdain.

"Let's get back to the ironing, " she said, "Your Mam'll think I'm not pulling me weight."

Reluctantly I put the tram ticket into the page and closed the book on hapless Dennis, sweet Jessie and scheming Eleanor. Auntie Bella delicately tested an iron with a spit-finger and sorted through the clean washing in the basket.

"Auntie Bella?" I said.

"That's me," she said absently.

"Uncle Freddie would never let you down like that," I said with all the seriousness of childhood.

Auntie Bella turned slowly with a familiar pair of back-vented drawers hanging from her hand.

"Don't mention that man's name in this house!" she said and an arctic blast whistled under the scullery door to chill my blood. Auntie Bella turned back to her ironing board and crushed the unfortunate drawers as though he whose name may not be mentioned was encased within. The fury of her assault made me wince.

"Why not?" I said, timidly, bravely.

"Because," she said, and folded the drawers with such ferocity one might almost hear bones breaking.

"I'm sure he can explain everything," I pleaded.

"Now see what you've made me do," said Auntie Bella, "I've a smut on that pillow case."

The article in question was at least six feet away. Auntie Bella laid the deeply depressed drawers aside and, looking at my anxious face, softened as she always

did. She picked up a large stack of fresh-smelling laundry and loaded me to my eyebrows.
"Would you take that lot up to your Mam?" she said, "And say I'm sorry I'm so behind, but it's all her son's fault."

It is all my fault. I've forgotten to explain. All the men in our ménage were in disgrace. Uncle Freddie, Our Dad, even poor Grandad Fergie. If you'll be patient I'll explain everything.

Out of Auntie Bella's kitchen door, out of the scullery, across to our bottom door, lift the snecks with your head, sneak a hand free to close the doors, open the door into our echoing bottom passage, and up the stairs onto our landing. I can still make this journey in my dreams. One day perhaps I'll make that journey again to climb our clattering stairs and find my Mother sitting sewing in our Room in Hurworth Place.

I would find myself on the landing with all three doors closed, kitchen, Room and bedroom, and because I was the imaginative child that I was, in the twilight of that creaky landing I would suddenly become afraid that my Mother wouldn't be there and I would call out for her to reassure myself.

"If you think," my Mother's voice said, "That I'm getting up to open the door for you."
She left the threat unfinished and I fumbled the Room door open to find her sitting in her chair with somebody's pillow slip in her lap. Nothing was ever returned in the wash that she didn't check every seam for missing stitches.
"What a bairn," she said, "We've only the one room, but he still cannot find me."
How could I explain that frightening space between the worlds, our landing?
"Auntie Bella sent these up," I explained unnecessarily and laid my burden down on my bed.
"Where did you think I was?"

I came to sit on the cracket where I could watch her fingers work the needle with stitches so small and precise you'd think a machine had done it. She was the most beautiful person in all the world to me and I see still the beauty in the careworn face that watches me anxiously from the sepia photograph that is all I have left of her. I can understand how Mr. MacAtominey delighted in calling my mother the Rose of Hurworth Place.

"There's only the kitchen and here," she said, her fingers never ceasing to work.
"It was so quiet," I explained.
"I don't use a hammer when I'm sewing."
"I just wish you weren't always working, Our Mam," I said.
One day I would come up the stairs and she wouldn't be there. My mother worked from dawn to midnight, washing, ironing, mending other people's linen. And I never noticed she was dying. She laughed at the very idea.

"You daft duck," she said, "Hard work never hurt anybody."
Not if you're built of cast iron it doesn't. But bronchial asthma when you're washing, possing, ironing all day long isn't a big help.
I said firmly, "When I'm rich I won't let you work any more. I'll get a lass in to do the possing for you. And the ironing. And we'll get a machine with a proper treadle for the sewing."
My reward was that she laughed out loud and lost a stitch at such a ridiculous notion.
"And the Tyne'll smell of roses," she answered, retrieving her stitch, "Anything to report from the nether regions before you forget?"
"Oh, yes, " I said, "We had quite a shock. Eleanor's got a swelling under her riding habit and Dennis has got the blame."
"I'm not even gona try to understand that," decided my mother.
I asked wistfully, "D'y'think it could be a cushion, Our Mam?"
"There's many a one wished that," she said and smiled to herself.

She sat in her chair, calm centre of the universe, sewing the heartbreaks back together again. I loved Our Mam with all my being and never told her once.

Hesitatingly, I said, "What if I mention Our Dad's name in this house?"
"If you must," said my mother.
She stopped sewing and looked at me. She reached forward and pushed the hair from my brow.
"I've told you. That's a scholar's forehead," she said sternly, "If you're not careful I'll put a clip in it."
Whenever she had to go to the Town Hall to pay, or more likely to explain, why we couldn't pay the rates, my mother always took me with her. When our business was concluded she would stop by a marble bust of some Greek philosopher or local philanthropist to compare brows which procedure I always found extremely embarrassing, but which was to my mother a cause of deep satisfaction.
I said, sadly, "You can't mention Uncle Freddie's name downstairs. Auntie

Bella's ironed his BVDs tighter than the whitewash on the wall."
"That must've hurt," said my mother with the merest hint of a smile.
"He gets his dinner," I said, "But Auntie Bella's definitely finished with him."
My mother stopped sewing, instantly aware, and said, cautiously, "Before you ask, Mister Machiavelli, the answer's no."
"Couldn't he come here?"
She said, "Over my dead body," and sewed calmly onwards.
"Don't you see?" I pleaded, "Auntie Bella would start to miss him."
"I very much doubt it," she said with a complete lack of feeling.
"Absence makes the heart grow fonder?"
"Out of sight, out of mind?" she parried.
"He'd be no bother?"
My mother said, "We can't be talking about the same man."
Repulsed, I gathered my forces for a counter attack, but my mother overran my front line, saying, "Besides I'm seriously thinking of getting shot of your Dad. I'd rather have an Eskimo round the house than that man."
I had to admit it was a very tempting offer. Our Dad was a difficult man to live with. I read about this Kentucky mountain man who shared a cave with a bear very amicably. He should've tried living with Our Dad.
"Are you serious, Our Mam?" I asked, anxiously, hopefully, trying to read her lowered face.
She bit off the knotted thread and said, with a straight face, not a hint of jollity, "Would I, your mother, joke about something like that?"

I never understood what Dads were for. At breakfast time Our Dad came home from the Co-op bakery in a bad temper and went to bed. At supper time he got up in a worse temper and went back to the bakery. I suppose the fact he lost a leg in Flanders at eighteen years old and spent the rest of his life at a baker's bench with the stump jammed into an ill-fitting metal tube might've had something to do with his erratic behaviour. But I was only a child.

Obviously matters had come to a serious head. Tentatively, I asked, "What about Grandad?"
Our Mam put aside the finished pillow case and reached for another.
"I'm giving him to the Reading Room," she said.
I nodded agreement.
"He'll never notice. But why're we getting an Eskimo?"
My mother reeled off a length of thread, bit it free from the bobbin and said, "When did you ever hear an Eskimo raise his voice?"
Her logic was impeccable. She calmly threaded her needle as I agreed, "In the

Encyclopaedia it's called the Silent North."
"There you are then," she said, "The very thing for us. And we'd never be short of fresh fish."
She began to sew, such sweet, tight, perfect stitches.
"What about the seal blubber?" I asked.
"We'd have no unhappy seals here," said my mother firmly, "They'd have everything their little hearts desired."
"Oh, be serious, Our Mam," I complained.
"Sorry. Well, he could boil his blubber down in the wash house copper and sell it round the back lanes. For face cream or frying."
Immediately I volunteered, "He could use my jamjar collection."
"And you could help with the dogs," my mother agreed, laying aside another pillow slip, and reaching for a sheet with a broken hem, "You'd like that. You could have your own whip."
"I know all about it," I said, excitedly, "It was in the Wizard. You shout mush, to get them going," and then I stopped, "But there's no snow."
"You could put wheels on the sledge," said my Mother, in a moment of inspiration, her needle moving swiftly, surely along the seam.
I sat on the cracket and reviewed the glowing future. I looked up into my mother's serene face as she finished the sheet hem and reached for an antimacassar with broken threads among the flowers.
"You'll know me next time," said she.
"Are you joking, Our Mam?" I asked.
"No," she said, decisively, taking her scissors to the falling petals, "No, I rather fancy an Eskimo. It'll make a bit of a change.

You, gentle reader, might be wondering what has brought about this wholesale demobilisation of the men of our households. It was Palmer's cranes. From anywhere in Jarrow you could see the four great transporter cranes of Palmer's shipyard. When I was first old enough to recognise them against the sky as we went down Ellison Street towards Palmer's Gate and the river, Uncle Freddie told me they were there to hold up the sky. That was why Mr. Palmer had them built. To hold up the sky for Jarrow. And when I asked, such a fearful bairn, what would happen if they fell down, he said they never would, never in a hundred years. He promised me when I grew to be old and grey I would still see Palmer's cranes holding up the sky over Jarrow. When I persisted in asking what would happen if the cranes fell, he laughed at the absurd idea and declared the sky'd come down on top of us like Chicken Licken and that'd be the end of Jarrow.

In 1933 the last ship left the Yard and in 1934 Palmer's closed forever, but just so long as the cranes stood Jarrow folk could kid themselves one day pigs would fly and the Yard open its gate again.

DISMANTLING BY THOS. WARD LTD., SHEFFIELD said the banners on the cranes so even the daftest might know it was finished. Palmer's and Jarrow both dismantled. They cut them to the limit with the flame and then hand-winched them from the barges. When they fell the noise was like the slamming of a door. The ground was littered with baby pigeons from the nests among the ironwork. The men from Sheffield went about their labour stamping on the mewling squabs. Leastways the folk of Jarrow could stop kidding themselves about a happy ending. All except Uncle Freddie and me. We believe the cranes are still there.

The day the cranes came down Uncle Freddie, Our Dad and Grandad got drunk and were brought home by the police after a riot in the street. They were brought home, to the shame of Our Mam, Bella and Granny Fergie, because there was no room for them in the iron hotel. All the cells were full of drunken shipwrights god-blessing Freddie Dean who, if rumour is to be believed, had provided free beer for one and all. It was a wake for Palmer's.

I said to Uncle Freddie, consolingly, "Mrs. Chamberlain often has the pollis round."
Uncle Freddie was not to be comforted. He returned the broken iron stanchion to the pile of scrap as if dropping a pebble into a pool and the echo awakened every echo in the tin roof.
"It's not the same, old son," he said.
"Mrs. Chamberlain once threw the fat pollis down her front stairs," I told him, encouragingly, "But instead of coming in a gang to get their own back, they decided to live and let live. They said they could take a joke."
Mrs. Chamberlain was the most formidable woman in Hurworth Place. The time she thought the coalie was cheating the weight she chased him half-way down Albert Road. She'd've caught him if one of her suspenders hadn't broken. When he finally crept back his coal had vanished and the Chamberlain bairns were riding chariot races round the lanes with his horse and cart.

We were standing in an empty, echoing workshop in the desolation that once was Palmer's great shipyard. The rain was hammering on the roof like demented shrapnel. There was the same air of numb despair as one sees in photographs of the Great War. A fearful battle had been fought and lost here. There was all the evidence of defeat. Only the dead had been tidied away.

Uncle Freddie was not to be comforted. He was, despite outward appearances, a moral man who knew he had disgraced himself and shamed his wife.
"No," he said, "The lasses have the right of it. No getting away from it. Shameful day. Delivered to the door by black Maria. Never thought to see it, old son. Cannot recommend it."
"What Auntie Bella doesn't understand, Uncle Freddie, is where you got the money from?"
He considered the question thoughtfully, sucking on his empty pipe.
"She could leastways ask."
He subsided to sit, hugging his ankles in the fashion of his tribe. I hunkered down beside him and we stared out from the desolate workshop at the bouncing rain. Out on the river a drowning launch passed seaward.
"She can't," I said, "cos your name cannot be mentioned in this house, but she's itching to know."
Uncle Freddie grinned and removed his pipe to allow the grin to expand into a smile.
"Well, best we keep her guessing, eh?" he said.
"Our Mam doesn't want to know, thank you very much. She's too ashamed. She's given Grandad to the Reading Room and she's getting shot of Our Dad. She's having an Eskimo instead."
Freddie nodded.
"Mary was always one for novelties," he said.
I hastened to assure him that he'd always have a share of the best fillets. He thanked me with his usual courtesy and then asked if I could keep a deadly secret.
Breathlessly, I assured him, "Cross me heart and swear to die, I'll eat me puddens if I lie."
"I don't think that'll be necessary," said my fellow conspirator, "Just don't mention it to the lasses."
I nodded my agreement and waited for him to continue. Uncle Freddie sucked his pipe thoughtfully and then began to speak.
"Well, we watched the tykes pull down the cranes and then your Grandad said, 'Haway, I'll stand yous a saveloy'n'dip.'"
"That was his beer money."
"Said he'd lost his appetite for beer," Uncle Freddie commented sadly.
"He must've been very upset to say that," I added.
"Anyway, I come out of Abel's porkshop. Corner of Staple Road," said Uncle Freddie, always a stickler for detail, "Balancing three saveloy'n'dips and I walked into a tram swinging round the corner."
I was scandalised at his foolish behaviour.

"You tell me never to step off that pavement," I cried, indignantly, "The way they race those trams round that corner! They all think they're Donald Campbell!"
"Thank you, Indignant of Dunston!" said Uncle Freddie, "D'y'want to hear this or not?"
Even the rain slackened its imbecile hammering to listen.
"There I am," recounted Uncle Freddie, "Bouncing along the side of the tram, hanging on to the dips, when a woman screams and the next thing I know a babby falls on iss!"
I hung on his every word, swinging by my fingertips.
"From where?" I cried, "Where'd the babby come from?"
I had heard of it raining cats and dogs, but never babies.
"From the top deck of the tram," replied my trusty Uncle, "A babby wrapped in swaddling clothes."
"Wha'did yi do?" I asked.
"What could I do?" he exclaimed, "I catched hold of the little begger!"
"Bravo!" I cried.
"The din was deafening! The woman up top is screaming blue murder, the babby's bawling in me lughole, the tram knocks iss for six, and the next thing this lorry's trying ti flatten iss!"
"Oh, no!" I cried, horror-stricken at this cacophony of calamity, "The poor babby!"
My Uncle Freddie snorted his indignation.
"Never mind the babby! What about me? Just managed to tap dance me way clear of the lorry when Rea's ice cream cart is offering to stop me and buy one!"
"Was the babby all right?" I cried in anguish.
"Screeching like a steam hooter, but I had a good grip on it," complained Uncle Freddie. He stuck a grimy finger in his ear and wriggled it about. "I think the little begger's done permanent damage, that's what I think."
Hugging my ankles I could've hugged him, but we weren't a demonstrative people.
"Oh, Uncle Freddie," I cried, "Don't you see? You're a hero!"
"Oh, aye? That's not your revered Auntie's opinion."
"I'll tell Auntie Bella as soon as we get home," I promised.
"Don't you dare," my Uncle threatened, "You promised."
"But don't you think..."
"When the tram finally stopped this woman come running back. Give me my babby! she screams. Glad to get shot of the thing, screeching and bawling. Away she goes. Both of them screaming blue murder. But worse was to follow," said Uncle Freddie, his countenance darkening like a cloud passing across the grey sea.

"Oh, no!" I cried, "What could be worse?"
"You won't believe this," said Uncle Freddie with furrowed brow.
"I will if you tell me!"
"Some crafty begger had made off with the saveloys. We looked everywhere. Your Grandad was hopping mad, I can tell yi. His life savings gone up in axle grease, yi might say," recalled Uncle Freddie and bit savagely on his empty pipe. I commiserated with him.
"Oh, that was mean, Uncle Freddie. But cheer up! Cheaters never prosper."
"No, they get to eat other folk's saveloys," he said, and reviewing the situation, "The mistake I made was letting go of the saveloys to catch that babby. But that's not all!"
"You mean there's worse still?"
"This old wifie come to ask for me name and address. I told her, no thanks, missus. Losing the saveloys was bad enough."
The loss of the juicy titbits from Jarrow's premier pork butcher had obviously hit this noble man hard. I offered consolation.
"There might've been a reward?" I suggested.
"Then this old wifie puts her hand in her bag. I thought first mebbes she's found the saveloys, but no. Then I think she's bringing out a snotrag to blow her nose, but, no, it's a five pound note," our hero continued morosely.
My eyes opened wider than Mr. Rose's camera shutter.
"A five pound note?"
"Here, take this, she says, and God bless you! And stuffs it in me hand," said Uncle Freddie, acting out this gracious gesture with such conviction that I expected to see a five pound note materialise in his palm.
"I've never even seen a five pound note," I said wistfully, fiscally.
"White. Big as a gent's hanky. I was dumbstruck. I was gona give it back, but your Dad and Grandad said after all we's lost the saveloys so."
"So what?" I said.
"We spent it on beer," said Uncle Freddie, shamefacedly, "The rest is history."
We sat in silence for a long rainy moment while I pondered on the outrageous folly our men had committed.
"I don't think I will tell Auntie Bella," I said finally, decidedly.
"A good decision," Uncle Freddie decided.
Looking out into the monsoon through which one could only just discern our sadly quiet river beyond the broken battlefield, I saw a human figure struggling against the downpour.
"Uncle Freddie, " I cried, "There's someone out there! He's gona get drownded!"
We both stood up and Freddie shouted, "Haway, man, ower here!"
The stranger, surprised, turned and seeing us, ran to join us in the shelter of the

workshop. He came in shaking himself like a wet dog, a tall man, bearded, in a long tweed overcoat and a homburg hat. Both the man and the homburg hat were strangers to Jarrow. The only other homburg in Jarrow was in Gatoff's window on a dummy many believed to be the Czar of Russia in hiding, swearing they had often seen him leave the window in the evening as Mrs. Gatoff let down the blind.

Uncle Freddie said, "Yi'll likely drown out there, man. Best bide a while with us. Leastways 'til the rain slackens."

"Thank you kindly," said the stranger, "You the watchman here?"

More intriguing still the stranger was an American. When he bowed his head to speak to Uncle Freddie the water ran from his hat brim as from a toby jug.

"He's my Uncle Freddie," I said. Living my fantasy life in the humid darkness of the Kino every Saturday afternoon I knew all about Americans.

"Yorra Yank, are yi?" asked Uncle Freddie who didn't go to the Kino every Saturday afternoon.

The big man laughed and said, "I guess that's what I am all right. A Yank. May I offer you a smoke?"

He offered my Uncle an open case that blinked like a heliograph. Although he hesitated, Uncle Freddie took a cheroot.

"Thank you," he said, and indicating his pipe, "D'y'mind?"

The American shrugged. My Uncle broke up the tobacco and filled his pipe. He accepted the proffered lighter, to stand wreathed in glorious blue smoke, with an expression on his face such as must flit across Bedouin countenances on arriving at an oasis.

I said, "Don't worry about me. I don't smoke."

The American laughed and said, "Salt's the name. T. Vosper Salt. Salt of the earth, that's me," offering his hand to Freddie who shook it firmly, saying, "Freddie. Freddie Dean. Formerly shipwright of this parish. This is my nephew, Lecky."

To ensure I wasn't left out of the conversation I said, "Uncle Freddie's never forgiven you."

Mr. Salt looked puzzled.

"Me? For what?"

"For you being late into the War."

Uncle Freddie coughed. The American laughed and wiped at the rain on his face.

"Not you personally, you understand," said my Uncle.

Mr. Salt said, "Hell, I come as quick as I could! Sixth United States Engineers. Building bridges for your Fifth Army. And it was raining then, I remember. Is that all it ever does over here?"

Uncle Freddie said, a little grudgingly, "Well, yi fought hard enough when yi did come. And died willingly enough."
Mr. Salt said, "That's sadly true. I lost my younger brother. Never could keep him out of trouble," and then, "You were there, Freddie?"
"I was there," my Uncle said.
The two men stood on common ground and eyed each other as comrades.
"What brings you to this blasted heath, Macbeth?" asked Vosper Salt.
"Used to work here. When there was work. What brings you here, Mr. Salt?"
The American looked out on the sodden desolation, and nodded.
"You could say I was looking for fresh employment."
Uncle Freddie snorted and said, "Ye must be daft!"
I was scandalised.
"Uncle Freddie!" I cried.
He was usually a well mannered man.
The American said, "I take no offence."
"Even for a yank yi take the biscuit," said my Uncle, bemused, "Looking for work here? There's no work here, man!"
He spoke these words as though tasting bitter gall and looked away into the rain.
"He doesn't mean it, Mr. Salt, " I pleaded, "It's just his way."
"Don't concern yourself, son," said Vosper Salt, "Let the man say his piece."
Uncle Freddie turned to ask, "What's your trade, Mr. Salt? Gramophones on the never-never, is it?"
The American laughed.
"Call me Vosper, Freddie. Everybody does."
"That doesn't make ye any the less a daft Yankee," argued my Uncle, "Looking for work in Jarrow?"
He shook his head sadly, doubting the big man's sanity.
"D'yi mind me asking your trade?"
"Steel," said Vosper Salt, "I'm a steel maker."
Uncle Freddie laughed out loud, but there was no music in his laughter.
"Why's that so funny, Uncle Freddie?" I asked and Vosper's face was asking the same question.
"Man, Jarrow has the best crew of steel makers in England! All unemployed!"
"Is that so?" said Vosper Salt.
Vosper Salt eyed my Uncle speculatively.
"You interest me, Freddie. As the Good Book says, I come among you a stranger. And you took me in out of the rain. Go on, friend, tell me more."
He held out the silver case again to my Uncle who hesitated and then accepted.
This time he didn't feed his pipe, but smoked it as he would've done in the

trenches with the cheroot tucked into his palm to keep it from the rain.
"Well, man, " said my Uncle Freddie, "What you're looking at was... and could be again...the greatest shipyard in the world. From the first iron ships built on the Tyne to the warships of the Great War no better ships were ever built anywhere than Palmer's."
I said, "Some people call Jarrow Palmerstown."
Vosper Salt nodded his understanding.
"A company town," he said.
"An independent shipyard owing nowt to nobody," my Uncle said, "Iron ore in at one quay from his own mines in Spain and ships out the other. Every ship was Palmer's from drawing board to draught."
"Everybody in Jarrow worked for Palmer's," I added.
"We had blast furnaces, steel works, rolling mills, boiler and engine shops! Why, man, even a gas works!"
Uncle Freddie's voice faltered as he recalled all that had been lost.
"What happened?" asked Vosper Salt.
"Independence was our weakness. The big boys ganged up and we were out in the cold."
Vosper Salt nodded his understanding.
"Happens in the States too," he said.
We stood looking out at the faltering rain. Somewhere above the grey clouds God was returning his watering can to the garden shed.
"Have yi lodgings for the night?" my Uncle asked.
"Well, no, Freddie, no, I haven't. I thought I'd..."
"Well, we haven't much, " said the damp-trousered philanthropist, "But I cannot leave yi here. Haway home with us."
An astonished Vosper Salt looked at Uncle Freddie.
"I don't think you understand."
Freddie took his arm.
"You're coming home with us," he said, "We cannot leave yi here, can we, Lecky?"
I shook my head in agreement.
"Our Mam and Auntie Bella would be very upset if we did."
They wouldn't turn away a stray dog would my Mother or my Auntie. Our Dad would without any hesitation. And send the cat along for company. But the women wouldn't. Somehow there would always be enough for another plate. They contrived this by taking it from their own.
Vosper Salt seemed genuinely moved by my Uncle Freddie's offer of a roof for the night.
"Thank you, Freddie," he said, "I'll accept your offer of hospitality if you're sure

my presence won't inconvenience your good lady wife."
"Nothing posh," said Freddie, "Just a shakedown. But better than a doss house."
I hastened to assure Mr. Salt that our house was heaps better than any doss house and we set off home through the final drizzling from God's watering can.
Auntie Bella wasn't in her kitchen so we went to the foot of our stairs and Uncle Freddie called up.
"Are yi there, Mary?"
"Whatever you do, Mr. Salt," I whispered, "Don't mention Uncle Freddie's name in this house."
"If you say so, son," whispered Vosper Salt, understandably puzzled, but I didn't have time to explain further.
My mother came out on the landing from the kitchen, and asked, "Is that you, Freddie?"
"There's nobody downstairs," he said, "Any chance of a warm?"
I saw Mr. Salt studying the interesting pattern of cracks in our bottom passage ceiling.
Our Mam said, "Bella's here. But I'm not so sure she wants yi up."
She consulted with Bella while Mr. Salt studied the lack of linoleum in our bottom passage.
"Look, Freddie," he said, "I wouldn't wish to," but my mother reappeared and said, "So long's you're showing the white flag yi can come up."
We started up the stairs and I explained to Vosper Salt, "It's because Uncle Freddie was brought home by the pollis," which, on reflection, wasn't a reassuring thing to say.
"Does that happen often?" whispered Vosper Salt.
"Who's that with yi?" my mother asked.
"Name's Vosper Salt. A Yankee and as daft as a brush," replied Uncle Freddie, "This'll give yi an idea how daft. He's looking for work!"
He laughed and woke the stair echoes.
"That means he likes you," I translated.
"Boy, I'd hate to hear what he'd say if he didn't," Vosper Salt replied.
As we climbed the stairs I stopped transfixed by the image of my mother on the candle-lit landing. She looked like an angel. She was so beautiful I couldn't breathe.
When Uncle Freddie and Mr. Salt reached the landing the American gravely shook my mother's hand, much to her embarrassment.
"How d'y'do, Mrs. Ferguson? I guess I am intruding on you. Just say the word and I'll march right out of here."
"No, you won't, Mr. Salt," she said, "It's a nasty night out. Besides we're used to Freddie and his stray dogs."

"That describes me to a tee, ma'am," our visitor said, and laughed.
My mother warmed to Mr. Salt, saying, "I'm sure you're not. Go on in. It's a sight warmer in the kitchen."
"Thank you, ma'am, if you're sure I'm not intruding?"
"Take us as you find us," my mother said, "We're not the Ritz."
Uncle Freddie and our guest went into the kitchen.
"Well? Are you coming or not, Dozy Dick?" asked my mother.
Then I realised I was still standing on the stairs. My mother lifted the candle to look at me. I looked at her, filled with an aching love I could not voice.
"Now what's up with you, bubbly jock?" she demanded.
"Nowt," I said defiantly, through my tears.
"Don't say 'nowt'. It's common. If you have to, say 'nothing.'"
"Nothing," I said, and came up the last stairs to her.
She regarded me sternly.
"It's a funny nowt that makes your eyes water," she commented, and putting a hand to me, complained, "You're wet through." She put a hand to my brow, absently, forever, pushing back the wet hair to display the classic brow that was her pride and joy.
"You feel cold to me. I'll tell that Freddie what I think of him," she said, turning to do just that.
"No, Our Mam, don't! It's not his fault. He doesn't work the rain, y'know," which I thought a pretty neat answer.
To which she responded, "You do surprise me. I thought your precious Uncle could do everything."
"Almost everything," I defended, loyally. I wanted to say, 'How bonny you are, how bonny.' I didn't, but I wish I had. But I couldn't and I didn't.
"Don't you be sick over me," she said fiercely.
"I won't," I said, "I don't feel sick."
"Well, you look it," she challenged, "Go in and get your other shirt out of the drawer. And change those trousers."
"Yes, Our Mam."
She turned to the kitchen door again from behind which voices rolled like waves on the shore, and then turning back to me, said, "This one Freddie's dragged in. Is he all right, d'y'think?"
It was a pleasure to assure her that the guest was housetrained.
"Oh, yes," I responded, "If he was on at the Kino he'd be doing Edward G. Robinson's part. He's got the hat and cigars."
"That's very reassuring," she said, "Go on then. Here. Take the candle. I know you and the dark."
"I'm not afraid of the dark."

"Oh, well," said she, "I'll keep the candle then."
"No, no, I'll take it," I said, reaching for the blessed flame.
Her hand on the kitchen door sneck she said, "And ca canny! Your Dad's not in the best of tempers," and when I hesitated, "Go on, scoot!"
I said, "You know about you getting shot of our Dad and having an Eskimo instead?"
She turned her head away and said, "Supposing I was."
I said, "Mr. Salt's lived with them."
"Oh, well, your father won't come as too much of a surprise then," my mother said.
"He'd put Granny out. Because of her teeth."
"Who would?"
"They go stiff as a board. There was this old woman leaning up against this igloo. With a frozen smile on her face."
My mother released the kitchen sneck and gave me her full attention.
"Right. I want to scream, but I won't. I'm a big lass. I'll try to be brave. Start again, Socrates. Why would my Eskimo put your Granny out of the house?"
"It's his natural custom when her teeth's worn down," I explained, "If she couldn't chew the skins any more."
"What skins?"
"Then there's the walrus fat. D'y'want to have that rubbed all over you?"
My mother said, "Finished?"
I said, "Yes, Our Mam."
She brushed the hair away from my alabaster brow, saying, "Don't plan anything for tomorrow."
"Why not?"
"Because you'll be busy," she said.
"With what?"
With the air of an executioner, she said, "It's senna pods for you, my son."
I stared at her in righteous indignation.
"But it's not the end of the month!" I cried.
"Then don't tell anybody," she said, "It'll only cause jealousy."
She disappeared into the kitchen before I could think of a suitable response.
Every last Sunday in the month my mother scoured us out with senna pods. Chipped cups and mugs stood on the kitchen table and everybody in our combined households swallowed the bitter draught. Nobody went far from home on scouring day. Everybody just hung around with frozen smiles.
When my father came into the kitchen all conversation stopped and silence fell with an iron clang. He stood behind his chair looking at Mr. Salt who was finishing his supper. Our guest started to rise, but my father said, "Sit down. Yi

might as well finish up," and Vosper Salt sat down and slowly cleaned the plate with a piece of bread, trying to understand what was expected of him.
Granny Fergie said, placatingly, "Sit down, Davie. Mary's got your dinner's here."
My father sat down and my mother brought his dinner from the oven. He filled his mouth and said, "Who's this then?"
My mother said, "This is Mr. Salt, Davie."
She knew from long experience that the less said when he first got up the better, but Grandad said, "He's a Yankee Freddie found down at Palmer's."
My father shovelled the mince and potatoes into his mouth steadily. Everybody breathed a little easier.
"Then what's he doing here?" said my father, amiably enough.
Granny Fergie said, "He's nowhere else to go, poor man."
My father stopped eating to say, "He could go back where he come from."
My grandfather said, "That's Jarrow hospitality, is it? Send them back where they come from? Most of Jarrow'd be on a boat for Eyerland."
I saw my mother share a glance with Auntie Bella. That's how my Granny and Grandad were, bobbing around our Dad like bairns round a bramble bush. Granny never remembered she wasn't his Mam any more. Grandad was his constant sparring partner. Flint and iron they were together.
"You're talking daft," said my father. I decided to intervene before the sparks flew.
"What do you call a woman with one leg longer than the other?" I offered.
My mother said, "Lecky!"
Undaunted I challenged them, "D'y'give up?"
There were no takers.
"Eileen," I said, "D'y'gerrit? I lean?"
"Do you want to go out on the landing?" my mother invited.
"I was only adding to the general air of jollity," I said indignantly.
"Then don't!"
Vosper Salt said, "I'm very pleased to meet you, Mr. Ferguson."
"Oh, aye?" questioned my father, "Why would that be?"
"You're very generous people and it's a privilege to be here," said Vosper Salt, "I thank you and your good lady wife for your hospitality, sir, I really do."
My father ignored our visitor and addressed my mother, refilling his mug of tea.
"And who might this Mister Salt be when he's at home?"
My mother, spooning sugar into his tea, said, "And who fell out of bed the wrong side tonight?"
"Are we running a boarding house?" my father demanded to know, "Is that it? How much do I owe you for the week, missus?"

He fumbled in his pocket as if he would pay her and the pain was clear in my mother's face.

My father's behaviour was completely unpredictable. On another evening he would've been as sweet as honey and generous to a fault, welcoming a stranger to his table. When I was older and my mother's restraining influence was gone he and I fought our war to a standstill. We were the best of enemies and the worst of friends. My father was a victim of that terrible war to end all wars. He survived the Somme on that aweful July day. He fought the battles of Passchendaele and Arras. He lost his brothers and his left leg. One night when he was drunk he told me he had left his soul in Flanders' mud along with his leg.

My mother said, placatingly, "Behave yourself, Davie. Mr. Salt's not come to steal the family jewels."

I said, "I never knew we had any!"

"Bit late for that," said my father, "National Shipbuilders've walked off with them."

My mother said to Vosper Salt, "Take no notice of him. He's only half-awake."

"This Yankee's a steelman, Davie," said Uncle Freddie, "Looking for work."

My father stopped chewing to say, "What loony bin has he escaped from?" and glared at Vosper Salt.

"Eat your dinner, Davie," my mother suggested, "You can glower at Mr. Salt while you're chewing," and to Vosper Salt, she said, "You'll have to forgive my husband, Mr. Salt. He's a darling man. But not much of a sunbeam this time of night."

Mr. Salt gestured understanding and my mother added, "Though he could make an effort for once."

"I'm in me own house," said my father, cleaning his plate.

My mother continued with, "He has the night shift at the bakery. It's not a natural life. We're just thankful he's in work."

I decided to chip in with my twopennorth, saying, "He's a hero. He lost his leg in the War."

"Wouldn't be a show without Punch," recited my father.

Auntie Bella suggested, "Sit down and hush up, Lecky," but Granny offered, proudly, "He won the Military Medal. For bravery" which brought a growl from my father.

"When you're all finished jabbering on," said my father, raising his mug of tea as a judge might raise his eyebrows, "P'rhaps we could find out why he's here."

The first witness for the defence stepped forward.

"Found him wandering round the Yard," said Uncle Freddie, "Couldn't leave him to drown."

"I never joke about business, sir," said Vosper Salt, "Freddie has convinced me that Jarrow is the place for my new enterprise."
"Eeh, Lecky, pet!" cried my grandmother, "It's him! The dark man in the tea leaves! It's him!"
Granny Fergie and I stared at one another hugging our secret knowledge. The tea leaves had scored another triumph.
My Auntie Bella had been very quiet, but now she asked, "Does he really mean what he says, Freddie?"
Vosper Salt smiled at her, "I surely do, ma'am."
Uncle Freddie recovered his scattered wits to say, "Why, man, this is the grandest news I ever heard! D'y'hear what he's saying, Davie? "
My father was more reluctant to believe. Doubting Davie would've fitted in nicely with the Apostles.
"Too good to be true," he said and swallowed the last of his tea.
"For the love of God, " said my mother, "Don't say anything you don't mean, Mr. Salt. Just the truth."
"That'd be a welcome change round here," said my father.
Mr Salt took my mother's hand and looked her straight in the eye.
"The men of Jarrow," he declared, "are going to make the best and cheapest steel in England. In my new steel works."
My father said, "Why would you come here?"
My father was aware that Vosper Steel was still holding my mother's hand. He relinquished it reluctantly.
"If I'm honest, to make money. For me and my shareholders. But I pay an honest day's pay for an honest day's work."
"Why not in Yankeeland," said his inquisitor.
"There's a war coming in Europe," said Vosper Salt. The gaslight flickered and a long shadow fell across the room.
"Oh!" said my mother, comprehending, "Is that the price of it?"
"Another war?" said Bella, and the shades of my father's lost brothers joined us in that little room.
"In five years time the demand for steel will be out of this world," said Vosper Salt.
"And so will thousands of mothers' sons, no doubt," said my mother and I saw the unforgiving sadness in my grandmother's face.
"Without the steel, ma'am," Vosper Salt said, "the Germans will win this time."
"Will it work?" asked Uncle Freddie, "The steelworks?"
"With the Bessemer open-hearth furnace and Jarrow sweat we'll produce steel at least one pound sterling per ton cheaper than the British Iron & Steel Federation," declared Vosper Salt.

The accused rose to his feet to make a personal statement.
"Vosper Salt, steelmaker, sir, of Pittsburgh, Pennsylvania."
Vosper offered his hand to my father who hesitated, but shook it firmly, saying, "Sit down, man, sit down. You make the place look untidy."
I said, "Mr. Salt, tell him about the eskimaux putting their grannies out in the cold when their teeth have worn down."
My mother said, "We can do without any nonsense, Lecky."
I desperately wanted to warn my father of what was going to happen to our family if my mother got rid of him and brought in an Eskimo. Perhaps he could make some fundamental changes to his behaviour and stave off catastrophe? Some hope. D'y'know his workmates argued to the management that a one-legged baker should take less money than a baker with two legs? That's the literal truth, swelp me God! So this proud, stubborn man, with yeast bags tied to his elbows and knees, crawled into the hot ovens every Sunday morning to sweep them out with a hand brush just to make up his money. Working class solidarity? Excuse me while I weep. So I doubted whether threats of being ousted by an Eskimo would make much difference to him.
I ignored my mother and pleaded with Vosper Salt.
"Tell him how you found that old wife leaning up against the igloo, frozen solid."
"Eeh, never!" said my grandmother.
"Stiff as a board. All because her teeth wore down," I explained, and seeing Granny Fergie's face, "Don't worry, Granny, I won't let it happen to you."
My mother took me by the arm and said, sweetly, "Lecky, sweetheart, d'y'want to go to bed?"
She never called me sweetheart.
"No," I said, "I want to -"
My mother interrupted and warned, with a flash of steel, "You're going the right way about it."
She gave my arm another vice-like squeeze and I surrendered.
"Don't say I didn't try to warn you, Our Dad!"
"Finished?" said my mother.
I nodded and she released my arm. The blood began to flow again.
"Let me explain myself," said Vosper Salt, "I'm looking to make work, Freddie. For you and hundreds like you."
My father delivered his verdict.
"He's talking daft," he said.
Vosper Salt continued, "I came to England looking for a place to open a new steelworks. I reckon I've found the right place. Thanks to Freddie."
"This some sort of Yankee joke?" queried my father.

There was silence in the kitchen as we dared to believe that Jarrow might be rescued from her sorry plight.
My grandfather contributed, "The government said, Jarrow must seek her own salvation. And here you are, in our kitchen. Jarrow's saviour. God bless you, sir!"
Granny Fergie bustled round with the big teapot, saying, "I'm sorry wi've nothing stronger to offer, Mr. Salt. Next time, p'rhaps?"
The great man laughed and raised his chipped mug in a toast.
"It's a cup shared among friends. Nothing better. But for a toast, I give you Freddie Dean. God bless him and every Jarrow man like him!"
We all toasted Uncle Freddie who had brought salvation to us. My father went off to work, labouring at a bench kneading dough, emptying ovens of clattering loaf tins, filling trays with hot fresh bread for a new dawn in Jarrow. A happy, but tearful Auntie Bella retreated downstairs with Vosper Salt and Uncle Freddie. It was the happiest of evenings, the beginning of a new era for Jarrow.
I climbed into bed and settled with my book. My mother sat in her chair with her sewing. If you asked me where I would wish to be in all the world, it would be that upper room in Hurworth Place, a child again, reading in bed, aware of my mother sewing in a pool of lamplight, in a sweet silence broken only by the falling of the coals and the occasional steam train on the line beyond the houses across Albert Road.
"Where's the end of the chapter?" said my mother.
"Next page," I said.
I read to the end of the chapter and closed the book on the tram ticket. I lay down to sleep and my mother came to swaddle me in the counterpane.
"Sleep tight," she said and kissed me.
"Don't let the bed bugs bite," I answered.
She turned down the gas and went back to her chair.
I said, "We could get used to walrus grease, Our Mam. It wouldn't be so bad. You could ride on the sledge and mebbe we could get false teeth for Granny?"
Without raising her head, she said, "I'll write first thing the morn and make enquiries."
It had been a very satisfactory day.
Next morning Vosper Salt took a train to London to negotiate with the Iron & Steel Federation and in the weeks that followed we resided happily in the kingdom of Euphoria. We were going to build Jerusalem anew in England's sad and sooty land and I was going to have an Eskimo for a father. It would make a nice change. I could hardly wait.
Then came the telegram boy to the door. I saw in my mother's face an echo of those terrible days when the boys were very busy pedalling grief in yellow envelopes to almost every house in every street in the kingdom. My mother and

I escorted the telegram upstairs to the kitchen where she laid the yellow envelope on the table. She took a deep breath and said, "Go and get Bella and Freddie."

I went downstairs and when we returned, my father had been roused from his bed and was standing in bodyshirt and trousers holding the telegram. Uncle Freddie nodded at him and my father opened the envelope. My mother sat down.

My father cleared his throat and read, "If convenient arrive Saturday stop if inconvenient stop reply Salt Savoy stop Vosper stop."

"What does it mean?" Auntie Bella asked.

I said, "Does he mean the Savoy picturehouse?"

"Be quiet," said my mother.

"Why does he keep stop-stopping?" I wondered.

My mother said, absently, "D'you want to go to bed?"

"You're always asking me that," I complained.

"What does it mean, Davie?" said my mother, echoing Auntie Bella.

"It means he's coming," my father answered.

"Is that all?" Auntie Bella asked, "Nothing about the steelworks?"

Uncle Freddie took the telegram from my father's hand and read it to himself. "He wouldn't put that in a telegram," he decided.

"Then it's bad news," Auntie Bella decided.

"No," said Uncle Freddie, "Vosper'll be here tomorrow. Then we'll know."

My father grunted significantly.

"And what's that supposed to mean?" asked my mother.

"Don't blame me if it all ends in tears," he said.

She gave him a look that would've melted paint.

"I'm going back to bed," he decided.

When he'd gone I said to Our Mam, "He'll be sorry once you-know-who gets here."

But all she said was, "Do you want to go to bed?"

I wondered whether Vosper would bring the Eskimo with him. Should I warn Our Dad to get packed? Or would it be kinder to let it come as a surprise? But when Vosper Salt came he was alone and we broke our necks from the front window to see the limousine and chauffeur at the kerb. Not that we were to be outdone. My mother had a feast fit for a prince set out in the Room. Boiled ham and a sponge cake. When Uncle Freddie brought him up we struggled to contain our excitement.

Vosper Salt looked at the tea table with its homemade doilies, and said, "I don't deserve this feast, Mrs. Ferguson, I surely don't."

"Oh, it's nothing," said my mother, "Just a bite."

"We got the ham on tick from Porter's," I informed the guest.
"Lecky!" said Auntie Bella.
"It's their best," I insisted on telling him, "She didn't really want to let it go on tick."
Our Dad said, "Lecky, shurrup! Sit down, man. You must be hungry after that journey."
Vosper Salt said slowly, "I can't sit at your table, Mrs. Ferguson."
"Why ever not?" said my mother.
"There won't be a Salt Steelworks in Jarrow," said our visitor, sadly.
The silence was deeper than tears could bear.
Finally my mother said, "Why not?"
"The Iron & Steel Federation won't allow it."
My mother said, "But they can't stop you, can they? It's a free country."
"That's a laugh," said my father sourly.
"The Iron & Steel Federation control steel production in this country. What they say, goes."
"God rot them all in hell!" cried my Uncle Freddie.
"Freddie!" said Auntie Bella, "Remember the bairn!"
Vosper Salt said, "Oh, I could make steel here all right, but they've set a levy on production."
"What does that mean?" said my father.
"For every ton of steel produced I would pay the Federation the difference in price between my steel and theirs."
My mother laughed without humour.
"But that's silly!" she declared.
"How much would that be?" Uncle Freddie asked.
"At least one pound sterling per ton."
"So, if you made, a thousand tons of steel in Jarrow," my mother calculated, "You'd have to pay them a thousand pounds?"
Vosper Salt said, "I calculate I'd be paying a ransom to those rascals of not less than one hundred and fifty thousand pounds per annum."

This sum was beyond our capacity to absorb. It might as well have been the distance from Hurworth Place to Pluto. But the implication of the statement was clear enough.
Vosper Salt said, "I'm sorry. I can't do business with these people. So, no steelworks for Jarrow."
There is a point beyond pain where there is no feeling. The word used to describe this limbo is despair.
"I'm truly sorry," said Vosper Salt.

"The buggers'd rather we starved," said Uncle Freddie and Auntie Bella didn't reprove his language.

Vosper Salt produced a newspaper and handed it to my mother. "This is a London newspaper. It's all in there. I wanted to be here before the news hit your local paper. I'll leave it with you."

My mother accepted the newspaper numbly and said, "Whatever's happened, Mr. Salt, please, sit down and have your tea with us."

"You cannot go without a bite," said Auntie Bella.

The American shook his head, saying, "I'm sorry, ladies, I cannot do that. I feel I've let you all down," and turning to my Uncle Freddie, he produced a wallet and made to give him money in crisp banknotes, saying, "Freddie, I want you to take this. It's a poor exchange, but - "

"We don't want your charity," said Uncle Freddie in a voice that would've frozen an Eskimo.

Vosper Salt explained, "It's not charity, Freddie. It's offered in friendship."

"Then don't offer it. I'd rather have the friendship."

Vosper Salt appealed to Auntie Bella and my mother, saying, "Mrs. Dean? Please, accept this gift. It's little enough. Mrs. Ferguson?"

The women were silent, my mother only shaking her head.

My father said, "Money can buy nowt in this house. And that's final."

And that settled it. Uncle Freddie went down with Vosper Salt to the car and we sat upstairs in silence. When my father tried to have his tea my mother snatched the very bread from his mouth and clashed his plate down so hard it broke. It was like Nebuchadnezzar's feast when the writing appeared through the whitewash on the wall and frightened off their appetites.

My mother picked up the newspaper and read the headline aloud, "FEDERATION KILLS STEELWORKS."

"Do we have to have this?" said my Auntie Bella who was close to tears.

"Read on, Mary," said my father who had endured worse from the Kaiser's artillery without flinching.

Uncle Freddie came quietly in to hear my mother read out, "Bitter Disappointment for Jarrow. Hopes of Employment dashed."

Auntie Bella clutched at straws and asked, "Well, p'rhaps it's just a hold-up? Does it mebbe say 'next year'?"

Freddie put his arm about her, saying, "It's finished, Bella. Don't you understand that?"

My mother continued to read aloud, "It is to be regretted that Mr. Vosper Salt and his consortium have been unable to persuade the Iron & Steel Federation of the economic necessity of building a new Steelworks at Jarrow. Mr. Salt declared that efforts would continue to open closed minds..."

"You see?" cried my Auntie Bella, "He said efforts would continue! P'rhaps next year?"
"The Prime Minister, Mr. Baldwin," my mother continued to read, "said there had been considerable discussion on the possibility of further steelworks for the North-East coast. A desire on the part of all concerned to be helpful!"
"Aye, to themsels," commented my father.
In a sudden blaze of anger, my mother said, "I know what I'd do with Baldwin's pipe!"
"What, Our Mam?" I asked, interested, "You don't smoke a pipe."
"Smoke it?" she cried, and turned a furious face upon me, obviously mistaking me for Mr. Baldwin momentarily, and then, "Oh, be quiet, you stupid bairn!"
Auntie Bella said, "Is that it then? 'Til there's another war?"
I hastened to reassure her, saying, "There'll never be another War. The last one was the War to end all wars."
"Do you want to go to bed?" said my mother automatically.
I ignored this tempting offer and persisted in reassuring Auntie Bella.
"Don't worry, Auntie Bella. All the fighting's done now at the League of Nations. They've got a specially built hall for it where people outside cannot hear the noise."
My mother ploughed on with her reading from the newspaper.
"'I want to say,' the Prime Minister continued, 'with regard to many statements that have been made, that there is no truth in any of the reports that either the banks or any other authorities interested in these matters are making a dead set to prevent anything of the kind being done in the area. It is not true.'"
"Eddie Fenwick's pipe burnt right through to his linings," I explained, "Mrs. Fenwick said where there's no sense there's no feeling."
I thought they'd be interested in what happened to Eddie Fenwick, but my mother said, through gritted teeth, "Are you doing it deliberately?"
"The best place for a pipe is on the mantelpiece," I told her.
"I'll put you on the mantelpiece in a minute," she said.
Returning her attention to the newspaper she said, "There you have it! It's not true, and that must be true because the Prime Minister's said it, that anybody has stopped the steelworks coming to Jarrow."
"It's just not coming, that's all," said my father.

There are terrible moments in the life of any family when a child cannot comprehend the enormity of what has happened. We stood, as did all the folk of Jarrow, at the bottom of a pit from which there seemed to be no escape. I did my best to add a little jollity to family life.
"If Shirley Temple was here," I said, "She'd dance and sing and cheer us all up

with her merry banter. I could sing for you. Then we could have some merry banter."

My father gave me a look that would've frightened a tiger and said, "I'll give you something to sing about in a minute."

Then my mother started to tear up Mr. Salt's newspaper.

"What're you doing, Mary?" asked Auntie Bella.

My mother paused in her labour long enough to say, "What'm I doing? Making bum paper. Mr. Baldwin and the rest of them are only fit to wipe our backsides with."

To my surprise the family burst out laughing and eager were the hands to tear the newspaper into strips. Laughing is always better than crying, but what a woman my mother was! Life had come and knocked us down flat again. But not my mother for long. Here she was, tearing the complacent faces in the newspaper into squares. With twine threaded through one corner with the bare bodkin, voila, a fresh supply of toilet tissue! Ready to hang from its dispenser: the netty nail.

"Ooh!" said Auntie Bella, "Let me give Mr. Baldwin a poke in the eye. I'm feeling really nasty!"

Seeing Uncle Freddie still dazed by yet another of life's dirty blows, my mother said, "Cheer up, Freddie! When's it ever been any different?"

Uncle Freddie said, "You're right, Mary. We're on our own."

"As usual," said my father.

"But we're not alone, are we?" said my mother and they looked at one another and knew nothing was lost so long as they stood together.

"Here, Freddie," she said, rummaging in her purse, "I've a shilling. Me last penny. Take Davie with yi and have a glass of beer."

The men both brightened up, plop, as when you put a match to the gas mantle. They headed for the stairs, scattering gratitude like dandelion parachutes.

"Not that you deserve it," Auntie Bella called after them.

When the dust had settled on the stairs, my mother said, "Let's have this table clear, Bella. I've no appetite."

I responded indignantly.

"I have. I'm starving!"

My mother paused from the gentle cacophony of crockery to say, "I'll find you something when you've been over to Porter's with the ham. Tell her it's never been touched by human hands."

"Because we keep a monkey in the kitchen," I finished for her.

"Don't tell her that," warned my mother, "She may not be in a jokey mood."

"Yi can try her with the cake after," suggested Auntie Bella.

"Oh, Our Mam," I cried, rich with disappointment, "Can't we keep the cake?"

"Tell her the funeral was cancelled," said my mother, rich in invention.
"What funeral?"
"Don't tempt me," she said warningly.
I lingered at the Room door to ask, "Does this mean we're not getting an Eskimo?"
"Postponed, my son," said that wise woman, my mother, "But only postponed. Not cancelled."
When I got back from Porter's where a small hiring fee for the ham and sponge cake was added to our account, I took the bum paper down the yard and hung it proudly on the nail. We were the only household in Hurworth Place with bum paper from London. From next-door's netty Mrs. Chamberlain joined in singing Animal Crackers in my Soup. Have you ever tried tap dancing sitting down? I told her we weren't getting an Eskimo after all. She said I could have Mr. Chamberlain to make up for the disappointment. I refused her kindly offer explaining that my mother didn't much like men whose greatest achievement was to belch like a bugle or who hung their socks out the window for an airing.
It had been a black day retrieved from disaster by my mother's courage, but the morrow held its own bombshell of surprises. Uncle Freddie and I were possing away happily in the yard when Auntie Bella appeared in the scullery door.
"Freddie Dean!" she cried in a voice tremulous with emotion that boded no good for man nor beast.
Transfixed with the spear of undefined guilt, we eyed each other, man and boy, desperately trying to remember what sins we had committed that hadn't caught up with us yet.
"Yes, my love?" said Uncle Freddie tentatively.
Auntie Bella stepped into the yard.
"Don't you 'my love' me, Freddie Dean!" she cried.
What terrible transgression had we transgressed?
"Not if you say not to, my love," replied the perplexed posser.
The outraged woman came to the poss tub and the poss stick slipped from my Uncle's hand.
"Is there something you have to tell me, Freddie Dean?" she enquired, her gaze burning a hole in his forehead.
"Not that I can think of right off," said my hapless Uncle, "Can you, Lecky?"
"Don't involve the bairn," said the inquisitor.
"Then I don't know what you want me to say, Bella," said my Uncle, helplessly, "Although I'm sure I'm guilty whatever it is. I throw myself on the mercy of the clippie mat."
He smiled weakly, but Auntie Bella regarded him coldly.
"You're going red, Freddie Dean."

"That's the possing," said my uncomfortable Uncle, "Bella, unless yi give me a clue how'm I to know what I'm supposed to've done?"
Auntie Bella struggled with her emotions, wiped away a hint of tears with her pinny hem, blew her nose on a slice of old shirt, and fixed her husband with a judicial stare.
"Yes?" said Uncle Freddie.
In a voice fraught with emotional debris, Auntie Bella said, "There's a decent, respectable woman on the doorstep come to see you about her daughter's baby."
Uncle Freddie's mouth fell open as the drawbridge from a castle, complete with rattle of chains.
"Her daughter's baby?"
"Oh, Freddie Dean," cried my dear Auntie Bella, "Have you let me down?"
Recognition ran through me like a discharge from an electric eel.
"Another woman's child!" I cried, "Auntie Bella, it's ANOTHER WOMAN'S CHILD! That's what Jessie says when Eleanor brings her baby to Dennis's door! Oh, Dennis, have you let me down?"
My Uncle Freddie said, "Lecky, be quiet!"
"How could you betray me…" I persisted.
Auntie Bella said, "Lecky! Well, Freddie Dean?"
"When I have given you the best months of my life and Jessie half-swoons as if stricken a mortal blow," I quoted excitedly.
"I'll give you a mortal blow in a minute," threatened my normally pacific Auntie, "Well, Freddie Dean?"
But there was no stopping me.
"And Eleanor says, And what do you mean to do about it? And Dennis goes pale and staggers back." I recited, astonished how closely life mirrored art.
My Uncle Freddie had most certainly gone pale and but for the presence of the mangle would certainly have staggered back from Auntie Bella's accusation.
"Bella, I don't know what to say," cried my bewildered Uncle.
"And Eleanor laughs bitterly. But you knew what to say when passion enflamed you, and then there's a row of asterisks," I ended lamely.
My Auntie Bella said, "I'm waiting for an explanation."
"Well, I think," I said, "it was Arnold the under-gardener. The baby's got the same bandy legs."
"Lecky, put a sock in it," begged my beleaguered Uncle Freddie, "This is serious!"
"Right!" decided my Auntie Bella, "To the front door! Quick march!"
We stumbled through the house to the front door outside which stood a middle-aged couple as accurately described by Auntie Bella.
"Here he is!" she cried, "Now let him deny it!"

To our mutual surprise the woman shrieked and hugged a bewildered Uncle Freddie, crying out, "Here he is! At last! My hero, my very own hero!"
Auntie Bella stood, nonplussed, the boot of bewilderment being now on the other foot.
"Hero? What's going on, Freddie?"
The woman turned from suffocating Uncle Freddie with hugs and kisses to say to her husband, "It's him, Reg! This is the very man who saved little Arthur!"
Uncle Freddie immediately disclaimed this honour.
"I didn't mean it," he said, "It was just an accident, believe me."
The husband now seized Uncle Freddie in a bear hug, clapping him on the back heartily enough to displace trapped wind, releasing him only to imprison his soapy mitt, saying, "Mind, but you've taken some finding, Mr. Dean, but champion, fair champion! Let me shake you by the hand, sir!"
Which he proceeded to do, most vigorously, as if working the village pump for a communal bath night.
Auntie Bella recovered herself enough to intervene.
"Before I shake him by the neck will somebody tell me what's going on?"
The good wife turned her attention to Auntie Bella, her face wearing a smile as golden as the Mayoral chain, to say, "You must be very proud of him, Mrs. Dean! He is a giant among men!" just as my mother appeared on our doorstep to enquire, "What's going on, Bella?"
"You tell me, Mary," responded my disoriented distaff, "Would you like to step inside, missus, and tell me what's been going on?"

So it was in Auntie Bella's kitchen that the whole story of Uncle Freddie catching the flying baby was unfolded. Mr. and Mrs. Bell's daughter had come up from Barnsley to display their first grandson, Arthur. The son-in-law was a pitman and Mr. Bell was the superintendent of Jarrow Tramways which was a disappointment to me as Mr. Bell was the spitting image of Beardsley of the Flying Squad, as pictured in the newspaper kindly donated to our netty by Vosper Salt. Grandad Fergie wasn't the only member of our household who read the netty newspaper.
"I said to Alice," quavered a tremulous Mrs. Bell, " I said, let me take the little love and..."
She was too overcome to continue, mopping her eyes with a souvenir handkerchief from Blackpool which was covertly much admired by my mother and Auntie Bella.
Mr. Bell took up the narrative, reporting, "Unfortunately my dear wife let little Arthur fall from the tram into the road."
He stopped to comfort his lady wife, patting her arm severely as if killing flies.

My mother echoed Auntie Bella's exclamation of horror, saying, "You were lucky he wasn't killed!"
Mr. Bell smiled at an embarrassed Uncle Freddie, leaning across to kill some flies on his knee, saying, "Only because this gallant gentleman ran across the road and caught little Arthur even as he fell."
Unbelieving, Auntie Bella asked, "Freddie? My Freddie?"
"The very same!" exclaimed Mr. Bell, "The tram knocked him down, but he rolled clear."
Mrs. Bell emerged from her prestigious handkerchief to report, "Holding little Arthur in the air. Out of harm's way."
With choral harmony, her husband added, shaking his head in admiration of a shrinking Uncle Freddie, "Totally disregarding his own safety!"
"A lorry missed him by inches!" sang his marital harmonist.
Every eye turned upon our deeply embarrassed hero of the hour.
"Well, I never!" said my mother.
Auntie Bella's face was glowing with pride.
"Oh, Freddie! And you never said a word! Why ever not?"
"Because," I said bitterly, " His name couldn't be mentioned in this house. That's why ever not!"
My Uncle Freddie shifted uncomfortably on his chair as if sitting on a box of crabs.
"They're making something out of nothing, Bella, honest!"
Mr. and Mrs. Bell had put their heads together. Now they turned beaming, grateful faces upon the reluctant hero.
Mr. Bell announced, "To show our gratitude I'd like to offer you, Freddie Dean, a position as conductor on one of our trams."
Auntie Bella was transfixed with delight.
"A job!" she cried, "On the trams! Oh, my!"
The illumination in the kitchen was dazzling with all those beaming faces.
"With the lifesaving act being from a Tramways vehicle," announced Mr. Bell, portentously, "Even though it was my own grandson, I feel justified in offering you a situation."
"A situation!" cried Auntie Bella, "Even better!"
My mother pressed her brother-in-law's hand and said, "Oh, Freddie, how marvellous! And well-deserved!"
Auntie Bella said, anxiously, "Well, Freddie? Thank the gentleman."
I could contain myself no longer. I burst out with, "We can go down to Shields Sands whenever we want!"
"Whenever we can afford the fare," my mother corrected me.
"Oh, Freddie," pleaded Auntie Bella, "Please, don't be so daft as to say no."

Uncle Freddie sat silent in his chair, uncomfortably aware of the true facts of the affair.
"Please, Freddie?"
No one took a breath. Solitary was the ticking of the tin alarum clock on the mantel piece. Finally my Uncle spoke.
"I've done nothing to deserve it," he said, slowly, and waved away the protests of the grandparents, "But I wouldn't be so daft as to say no to the offer of a job. Thank you, Mr. Bell."
Joy was unrestrained. All the bells of heaven rang out in that humble home. Never was my Uncle more soundly kissed and hugged and hand-wrung as on that occasion. When the Bells rose to leave the last word was with Mr. Bell, the grateful grandfather.
"Mrs. Dean," he said, "Send your man down to the Swinburne Street sheds tomorrow at seven ack emma, and I'll start him on."

Well, that's how my Uncle Freddie became a tram conductor and that Christmas and for many another there was always a card from Worsbrough Dale, Yorkshire. It would be inscribed With eternal gratitude, Harold and Alice Scargill. And with the first card there was a snapshot of little Arthur with a miner's helmet and his own little pick and shovel.

So you see Granny Fergie was right and wrong after all. It wasn't Vosper Salt who was the dark man foreseen in the tea leaves, but the story I've told you about the invisible steelworks is the simple truth of how Jarrow was betrayed a second time. It was Mr. Bell, the Tramways Superintendent, who was the dark deliverer. And everything did turn out well. In the end.

For me Palmer's cranes haven't fallen. I see the great transporter cranes as they will always be, holding up the sky over Jarrow. Long shadows falling sentry across the darkening river as the day dwindles. I'm sorry if you cannot see them, for they are there, iron-dark against the grey sky, just as Babylon is and Lyonesse. As they will always be, unbroken, high above the cobbled streets of Jarrow, holding up the sky forever just as Uncle Freddie said they would.

Our Mam's Birthday

At dawn on Thursday, 21st March, 1918, the Germans, aided by thick fog, overwhelmed the British forward positions, breaking the line. It seemed the Kaiser would win the war after all despite the endless sacrifice and slaughter. My father was one of a raggle-taggle band of Scottish Riflemen and Yorkshire tykes who decided otherwise and stood to fight, to stop the flood pouring through the broken dam. With this defiant gesture they shocked the advancing Germans and held the line, breaking the momentum of the assault. My father and his comrades survived the ensuing counter-attacks and waited for reinforcement.

Davie Ferguson was a seasoned soldier, a company runner who had borne a charmed life throughout the shambles of Passchendaele, running in and out of the battle as if he were running errands for his mother to the shops. He told me that if a trench was blocked he simply climbed out and ploughed on through the porridge of the battlefield. Running out of a battle I can understand, but turning round and running back into the artillery barrage with a rice paper message is beyond my comprehension. Yet he did this again and again unscathed while every other runner died. This is a distinction he shares with Adolf Hitler. But you have to remember he was only eighteen and as daft as the proverbial yard broom. He was awarded the Military Medal for his bravery and men would touch his collar for luck as they passed him in the trench.

So you can appreciate that my father was the obvious choice of the young lieutenant to send back into the blasted heath from which his raggle taggle heroes had just retreated to see if company headquarters knew what the hell was going on. Or even if CHQ was still there. Don't bother to question the logic of the lieutenant's order. In the smoke and confusion of battle the young man had no idea of the enormity of the debacle that had overtaken the Fifth Army on that terrible morning. So away went Davie Ferguson, running like a fox stalking a rabbit warren, towards the enemy while any sensible man would be running like billyho in the opposite direction.

My father found CHQ deserted, but decided that while he was out for a stroll he might as well pay a visit to the shell-shocked house where he'd abandoned his kit when the line was overwhelmed. He climbed in through the glassless window and went to where his kit lay in a corner. A soldier appeared in the window behind him and spoke to him. My father replied reassuringly, picked up his kit and went to the window. Loaded with his kit as he was, the soldier outside gave him a welcome hand over the window sill. Once outside Davie Ferguson found himself surrounded by grinning farm boys much of his own age, but dressed in field grey. They laughed at his discomfort, but it was a fair cop, wasn't it? What I don't understand is why those boys didn't kill my father, bayoneting him as he stepped helpless from the window.

On the way back to the German position a British shell landed among those boys killing most of them and blowing away my father's left leg. So he ended up in a German field hospital side by side with the surviving wounded of that patrol to whose basic decency I owe my very existence.

I wasn't aware of this tragic irony until it was too late to repair the relationship between myself and my father, but I treasure every happy memory of him, though few and far between they may be. Just don't expect me to hate the Germans.

So it was one dark October afternoon when our story begins, a day when light died early and the world seemed even bleaker and more hostile than it appears in sepia postcards of Jarrow war memorial plus one old woman, a dog and a man pushing a handcart. Yet we were snug and happy upstairs in our kitchen, Our Dad, Auntie Bella and me.
"There y'are," declared my father, "X marks the spot."
We gazed upon one another, my father pleased with what he had accomplished, myself anxious to please.
"Yi don't think you're a bit old for daftness, Davie?" Auntie Bella enquired.
I hastened to reassure her.
"No, he's not," I said, "Granny says he could do with a bit daftness more often."
My father regarded me severely and solemnly declared, "Sworn to silence you are, Lecky. If you blab!"

"I won't!" I cried, "I promise, Our Dad."

We were engaged in a conspiracy against my mother. My father was decorating a cake with icing for her birthday. To secure the heart-palpitating surprise for my mother he planned, he had just marked a red cross in blood on my forehead. Or perhaps it was cochineal?

"If you blab," my father continued grimly, "your eye balls'll drop out of your head and roll under the sideboard and you'll never find them again."

This was a truly horrendous threat for I remembered the dread day when one of Granny Fergie's suspender buttons popped and shot under the sideboard. Despite our best combined efforts we never found that button although we did discover a used cough lozenge, a ha'penny stamp, unused, the lid of a Beecham's Pills box and a rusty kilt pin. Granny Fergie sucked the lozenge as she adapted the pin to salvage her dignity.

"If," declared my father, with savage relish, "and it's a big 'IF', you should chance upon your eye balls they would be covered with fluff. And you would have to lick it all off!"

This was the sort of stimulating conversation I enjoyed, but Auntie Bella protested.

"Davie! Is that necessary?"

My father gazed at my mild-mannered Auntie in amazement.

"Abso-bally-lutely, Bella! You are sworn, Lecky, unto death do part your hair. Comprendy?"

I nodded gravely.

"Comprendy," I replied.

We were a bi-lingual family.

"You pair are the giddy limit," Auntie Bella concluded shaking her head at our silliness, "I don't know which of yis is the daftest.".

My father and I exchanged smiles. I never understood my father. I think I loved him. I know I was deliriously happy just to be in his company and sharing this wonderful moment.

"She must not suspect we're up to someat," declared my father, "It'll be a wonderful surprise for her birthday."

"And I shall give her the most wonderful present she's ever had," I decided.

"And what'll that be?" Auntie Bella asked.

"I'm not sure. But it'll be the special-est present ever in all her life."

So there we were, happy and secure from that grey afternoon, watching my father with a savoy bag in his hand decorate the birthday cake. Tongue protruding, creaking on his wayward tin leg, he revolved the cake stand with one hand and created a froth of sugar beauty with the other. We held our breath

until he'd finished, straightened his back, and said, "Well? Wha'd'y'think? Will that do, mebbe?"
Auntie Bella smiled at his earnest simplicity, saying, "Yi make it look so easy, Davie. But it's a work of art."
"Well?" he said, frowning at me as if I were the art critic of the Manchester Guardian, "Well? Lost your tongue?"
I was lost in admiration. If ever you should contemplate losing yourself I would recommend admiration above despair.
"It's beautiful, our Dad," I admitted, "I bet there's not a better cake anywhere in Jarrow. In the whole world even."
My father frowned and looked to Auntie Bella.
She said, "He's taken the words out of my mouth."
"She won't want to cut it," I declared, "She'll say it's too good to eat."
My father gestured with the limp savoy bag and I opened my mouth. He squeezed the last of the snowy icing onto my tongue, saying, "Well, that's what it's for."
I heard Uncle Freddie's voice from the bottom passage and his boots on the stairs. I went to open the Room door, calling, "Come and see Our Mam's cake, Uncle Freddie!"
"That's right," complained my father, "Tell the whole world!"
When Uncle Freddie came in, my Auntie said, "Have a look at this, Freddie."
"It's just a cake, Bella," said my father, mixing cochineal and icing to pipe a birthday greeting, "Not the Taj Mahal."
My uncle regarded the cake in silence.
"Well?" I said, impatient for my father to be complimented.
Uncle Freddie said, "They're barmy to keep you filling ovens when you could be doing this, Davie."
"Aye, well," said my father, pleased, "What shall we have in the middle? Happy Birthday?"
"She knows it's her birthday," said I.
"What then?" he said.
I offered, "Have her name."
"Her name?" he questioned.
I explained, "So it's specially hers. From you. And all of us."
My father looked at Uncle Freddie who said, "He's got a point."
"Mebbe you're right," said my father, "Let's have a think."
He stood for a moment, deep in thought, with his tongue searching for the end of his nose, then bent and wrote swiftly with the nozzle on the cake.
"How about that?"
He turned the wheel so we could read the inscription.

"That's fine, Davie," said Auntie Bella.
"Couldn't be bettered," my uncle said.
"Mary, Queen of all our Hearts," I read aloud, "I wish I'd thought of that."
Uncle Freddie said, " I wish I knew why you've got a big red cross painted on your forehead, old son, but I'm not gona ask."

Then we heard my mother's hand scrabbling through the letter box to reach the key on its string behind the front door. Auntie Bella and Uncle Freddie went down to delay her while my father hid the cake and we cleared up the evidence. We were standing, trying not to giggle, when my mother struggled into the kitchen carrying the burden of linen Mrs. Gordon wanted making over for her daughter's wedding.
"Couldn't one of yi," asked my mother, "have given me a hand?"
"Sorry, Mary," said my father, humble as a schoolboy, "Didn't think."
She dumped her brown paper parcels, unmollified.
"Does nobody ever think of putting the kettle on in this house?"
My father hefted the kettle to find it empty and turned on me, accusingly, to say, "I'm warning you."
I hadn't said a word. I was wrestling with the moral dilemma that while we were enjoying ourselves my mother had been struggling from Tyne Dock with two heavy packages of linen. My happiness was dashed. It felt shabby and undeserved.
"Well?" said my mother as my father left the kitchen to fill the kettle.
"Well what?"
She fixed me with a look as sharp as her needle.
"What's he warning you about?"
"Nothing," I cried, alarmed, "He's just warning me in case there's anything to warn me about, but there isn't anything."
"You look very suspicious to me," she declared, poking the kitchen fire when she'd rather have poked me, to bring it to order.
I gave her my wide-eyed innocent look, borrowed from Jackie Coogan.
"Nothing, our Mam! Honest!"
She sneered at me out of her tiredness.
"Honest? With a big red cross on your face? What's that supposed to be? Well?"
In a mad moment, I said, "It's my nurse's outfit, our Mam!"
She stopped punishing the fire and laid down the poker. She gave me a look that might've passed for pity.
"Nurse's outfit?" she repeated.
"I know I've never said it, but I've always wanted a nurse's outfit," I improvised desperately.

She sighed, shaking her head, and said, "I worry about you sometimes, son. P'rhaps I should worry more."

She took a long look at me and said, "We could go one better. D'y'fancy a lass's frock?"

"No!" I said indignantly and started for the kitchen door.

"Where d'y'think you're going?"

"Practice bandaging."

"You can practice washing your face. Then you can practice getting your night shirt on."

"Aw, our Mam!" I protested, but I knew it was in vain.

"Wash! Bed! Now!" she recited, and when I moved reluctantly to the door, "I know you've been up to someat, Florence Nightingale. Doubtless I'll find out. And when I do y'can look out for flying bedpans!"

I passed my father in the doorway who glared at me as if I had sold the pass to the Persians. I began to fear for my eyeballs.

"And you can forget the nurse's outfit!" she threatened.

"What nurse's outfit?" my father thundered and fixed me with the basilisk gaze the Dutch Customs officer must've given the fleeing Kaiser on the eleventh of November, 1918.

Not in a long lifetime have I solved the dilemma of how you're supposed to feel when, being happy with a loved one, you find another cherished being is unhappy.

The next morning, resolved to ensure that my mother should have the very best of birthday presents I went downstairs to interfere with Auntie Bella's orderly life. After a lively discussion we decided the one thing lacking in my mother's life was a panholder knitted in cheery colours. However the process of creating this desired article was more difficult than I bargained for.

Patiently, my Auntie Bella explained for the tenth time, "Take the wool round the needle. Make a little loop and Freddie's your uncle!"

With my tongue seeking the end of my nose in unconscious imitation of my father I wrestled with the recalcitrant wool.

"Oh, Auntie Bella," I cried, "I cannot do it. It goes all wrong!"

She sat like Patience on a kitchen chair and regarded me calmly. I couldn't see how she could be so placid in this whirlwind of wool.

"With a bit practice, Lecky," she said, firmly but kindly, "You could knit her a lovely panholder. In red, white and blue. Very patriotic."

I regarded the unlovely tangle of wool.

"Are you sure it's what she wants?"

"It's what she needs. All she's got is that raggy bit thing. Besides when the soldier boys come marching down the street. Or the Prince of Wales mebbe. She

can wave it out the window. Two for the price of one!"
She sounded so encouraging I shrugged off the tangled jungle vine that was wrapping itself round my needles and accepted her invitation.
"Here, let me show yi again!"
I watched her dextrous fingers manipulate wool and needles as to the manner born. Left to herself she would've knitted me a panholder faster than Bluebird could cover Bonneville Flats.
"I do it right," I said, virtuously, "And then the wool goes wrong. Are you sure it's the right wool for knitting?"
"Have patience," said my kindly aunt, knitting in slow motion, "Rome wasn't built in a day."
"I don't want to build Rome," I replied, struggling with an inward vision of a knitted Coliseum slowly collapsing like a sloughed scarf, "I want to make a patriotic panholder that she can wave at the Prince of Wales."
"Then look at what I'm doing," said Auntie Bella, testing the patience of her sainthood.
"I am looking," I said, indignantly, "I'm looking very hard. But you're doing it so slowly I keep forgetting what you did before."
Auntie Bella pulled half a panholder from the needles before I could stop her and handed me the needles.
"Stick your tongue back in your head," she said, "Put your needle in the stitch. Wrap the wool round. Pull it through and then drop it off."
I got the bit about returning my tongue to its cave right, but nothing else.
"Oh, it all drops off," I cried, and handed the needles to Auntie Bella, "I'm not a lass, that's why. Their hands must be different."
My respected auntie sighed and said, with an odd significance, "P'rhaps their heads are different."
"It's no good," I admitted, "I'll never learn to knit."
I was a lucky child to have my Auntie Bella. When my mother was dying this ferrous fragmentiser of a woman carried her up and down our stairs to enjoy the pavement sunshine, determined she should live. Perhaps she loved me best of all. She still bought me the FILM FUN ANNUAL when I was fifteen and I'm not embarrassed to say I enjoyed it.
"Well," suggested Auntie Bella, not to be defeated, "Nil Dickie Randle! What about a bonny vase for your Mam to put flowers in? You could get some flowers from the chuggy bank?"
I had a vision of a potter's wheel in the back yard, as illustrated in the Children's Encyclopaedia, with myself as the jolly potter pedalling away to turn out not only Ming vases for every window sill, but capacious chamber pots for the incontinent inhabitants of Hurworth Place.

"Where we going to get the potter's wheel from?"
"Yi don't need one," said my auntie, "Yi take a milk bottle and you stick pictures on it. You'd never know it was a milk bottle when yi've finished."
"I would," I said, watching the potter pedal his wheel down back into the Encyclopaedia, "I don't want her to have a milk bottle with pictures stuck on. I want her to have the best present she ever had. I want to show her that I"
"Wha'd'y'want to show her?" asked Auntie Bella.
"I must go and see a man about a dog," I said and fled the kitchen.

If Auntie Bella couldn't help me, then perhaps Grandad Fergie could. He had an undoubted asset that we might put to use: a magnificent baritone voice. If you've never heard my grandfather sing, "I'll Walk Beside You", unaccompanied, then you've never felt the brush of angel wings. Although the old gentleman was willing enough to help all did not go well in that department either. Consequently at dinnertime in our kitchen as we enjoyed Auntie Bella's delectable broth I pondered on how to explain his involuntary absence from our table.

My mother fretted and said, "He's taking his time is your Grandad. I'll not keep his broth hot if he's reading down the yard."
"I thought we'd made a rule," said Auntie Bella, "He had to leave his specs outside."
"Go down and roust him out, Lecky," said my mother.
I rose reluctantly.
"Go on!" she insisted.
I said, "He's not in the netty, our Mam."
"Well, he left the house with you," said Auntie Bella, reasonably, as if talking about an old dog.
My mother looked at me sharply.
"Have you lost him?"
"No," I said, "Not exactly."
"How'd'y'mean 'not exactly'? Either you've lost him or you haven't. Which is it?" she said, as sharp as any King's Counsel.
"He's all right," I assured her.
"How can you say that?" said Auntie Bella.
"He said not to worry, but he won't be home for his dinner. Profuse apologies to the ladies, he said. Profuse apologies."
My mother leant across the table and hit me on the skull with her spoon. I cried out in pain. Believe me, the Spanish Inquisition would've got at the truth quicker if they'd used a spoon. My head was ringing like a church bell.

"I'll profuse apologies you!" my mother cried, "Where's your daft Grandad?"
I gazed at her reproachfully.
"You can give people conclusions hitting them with a spoon," I accused her.
"I'll conclude you in a minute," my maternal parent threatened, the spoon hovering for another stinging blow, "Where is he?"
"He said not to say," I muttered and prepared for another shattering blow to the cranium.
When I opened my eyes I saw that my mother had put down her spoon.
She said, sadly, "I hope it's not the drink. We don't want to start that again, Bella."
The sisters gazed fearfully at one another.
My mother said, "Tell me, Lecky, did you leave him in a bar?"
Desperately I responded, "I'm sworn not to say. He said it would only upset you."
"How right he was!" my mother cried angrily, "If you don't tell me this instant, I'll"
She paused, hunting a suitably horrendous threat. With a wild inspiration Auntie Bella cried, "We'll get the pollis!"
"The pollis?" said my mother.
"Well," I said, both relieved and reluctant, "Seeing how you've guessed. That's where he is."
The silence lasted an eternity as the two women stared at me and then at each other.
Auntie Bella said, cautiously, "What's your Grandad doing with the pollis?"
"They've locked him up," I said.
"Thank God, Granny's not here," said my mother.
"What's he done?" asked Auntie Bella.
I said, slowly, "He was singing."
Auntie Bella asked, "Since when was that a crime?"
My mother said, "Where was he singing?"
"In the street," I said.
"Why?" asked my mother.
It was a difficult question to answer.
"Why?" she repeated, "Why was he singing in the street?"
I said, shamefacedly, "I wanted money. To buy something and he said - "
"I knew you'd be at the bottom of this," said my mother. Auntie Bella was about to say something and then decided otherwise.
"That's why he was dolled up when they went out," she said and looked at me reproachfully.
"Where was he holding this outdoor concert?" enquired the prosecuting counsel.

"Outside the Ben Lomond," I said shamefacedly. It had seemed such a wonderful, magical adventure at the time. My grandfather had been the prime instigator. 'All in a good cause,' he had said, 'but not a word to the ladies'. And out of the backyard door we had fled, laughing together. How wonderful to be engaged in such a joyous prank!

My mother looked upon me with contempt and distaste.

"You'd have your grandfather singing outside a public house because you wanted money for spends?" she enquired.

"But he wanted to," I cried, close to tears.

I was ready to blurt out the truth of the whole shameful episode, but Auntie Bella said, "Grandad wouldn't have wanted much excuse to sing, Mary. At least he wasn't inside the Ben Lomond."

My mother seemed slightly mollified by this remark.

"He didn't go in?" she asked.

"No," I said, "When he'd finished singing I took the hat round and then he asked for requests. There was a lot of clapping and cheering."

He was a brave old man, wasn't he? Can you imagine him standing by the Longmore fountain? Across the road from the Ben Lomond? Dapper Dan, spick and span, pulling the idle men out of the bar, diverting the women from their shopping in Ellison Street, singing as sweet and clear as a linty in the salt and sooty air? All for his beloved grandson to buy his mother a birthday present. How daft can you get?

"Was he singing well?" asked Auntie Bella, forgetting herself.

"Oh, he was singing fine, he really was!" I cried fervently.

"Then why did the pollis lock him up?" enquired the prosecuting counsel.

"Oh, not for the singing," I assured her, "For the fighting."

There was another long silence in court broken only by a less harmonious voice than my grandfather's rising from the neighbouring yard where Mrs. Chamberlain implored her lover to return to her before she died of love forsaken as she worked at her mangle.

"What fighting?" asked my mother, cautiously.

"When the pollis came," I replied.

"The pollis came?"

"He told Grandad to move on."

Auntie Bella said, "Wouldn't the daft man go?"

She looked at her sister who said, "Surely he had enough sense for that?"

I assured them, "Oh, Grandad would've gone. The pollis even let him finish Beautiful Dreamer. He even clapped. It was the men from the Ben Lomond wouldn't let him go. They said it's a free country."

My mother snorted, "Only if you do what you're told."

"So didn't the pollis stop your Grandad?" asked Auntie Bella.
"He couldn't. Buckie Tallach threw his helmet over into Christ Church."
Auntie Bella said, "Oh, that must've been a big help!"
"The pollis said, 'Right! Which of yis is going over to fetch it back?' And Buckie said, 'It's not our hat, but, fair's fair, wi'll help yi get it back.'" I reported faithfully.
"Well, thank God for that!" said Auntie Bella.
"So they threw the pollis over the railings into Christ Church to get his hat."
"And then?" the prosecuting counsel demanded.
"And then that's when it really started. That pollis came back with a lot more. There was fighting all over Grange Road. Then they threw everybody in the black maria. It was the best fight I've ever seen."
Auntie Bella asked, "But your Grandad wasn't fighting, surely?"
"They put him in the black maria first. For starting it. But he had a good view."
Auntie Bella was scandalised.
"Locked up for starting a riot," she cried, "And he enjoyed it!"
"Profuse apologies to the ladies," I said on his behalf.
My mother said, "Was it about that stupid nurse's outfit I told yi you couldn't have?"
What could I say? I could feel the horns of the dilemma boring ever deeper into my very being.
"Well, I hope you're satisfied," she concluded.
"I hope the magistrate's impressed with his best bib and tucker," said Auntie Bella.
My mother commented, resignedly, "Let's hope he takes his hat off and smarms about a bit."
"I've got his hat," I admitted, "It's in the landing cupboard.

On a bright sunny morning in Grange Road sometimes still I hear the old man singing. The fountain's gone. The Ben Lomond's no longer the Ben. But sometimes it catches me unaware, that wonderful voice, singing like a magic linty, drawing the men to leave their beer and come out to listen to my grandfather singing.

There was sixpence ha'penny in the old man's hat. My mother, Mary Ferguson, was a brave and resourceful woman who knew there was a time to stop and share what comfort was at hand. The street singer, clasped in the clutches of the constabulary, was in no danger. The only threat to his life and limb was if his son, my father, should learn what tomfoolery the old man had been engaged in.

"The big jug, Lecky," ordered my mother, "and away toot sweet to the jug'n'bottle."
"You're not gona spend his money?" I exclaimed.
"Oh, yes, we are! Best stout, if you please," she insisted, "And make sure she fills it to the brim. No sipping on the way back. I can tell when you've been at it."
"I never!" I cried indignantly, "You can smell me breath if you like."
"No, thank you," she said, and noting my bewilderment, "It's all right. We're due a little treat."
"D'y'think we should?" Auntie Bella asked, daringly.
"Why not?" said my mother, "We'll drink to old Davie's health. If not his sanity."

And so they did, Mary and Bella, sharing the jug of happiness between them, laughing and chattering, shedding the cares of their everyday world, becoming again, strangers to me, the two carefree sisters they must've been in adolescence. When finally I spoke, breaking the spell, they looked at me as if I were a stranger. Then they remembered who they had become and rose reluctantly to return to the drudgery of the poss tub and the wash board, the flat iron and the needle. But for a moment I glimpsed the springtime of their lives and for a moment they remembered that joyous interlude. On the other hand I'd lost the sixpence I intended to spend on my mother's birthday present.

We walked on fairy tiptoe when my father rose to eat his supper, but he never even noticed Grandad's absence. When finally he went to his work, casting suspicious glances about him at all the glassy smiles, we three conspirators breathed a sigh of relief and an echo of sweet stout. When Uncle Freddie came home from his day on the trams he and I went down to the police station to rescue my grandfather. My mother's instructions were quite explicit. If they insisted on keeping him overnight they were welcome to him, but he'd need a chamber pot, a big one. They were not to keep him on the treadmill too long because it would only bring on his breathlessness and would they make sure he hung his suit on a hanger before chaining him to the wall.

When we got to the police station we found the front door was locked.
"They're shut, Uncle Freddie," I said, surprised.
He shook the door handle until I feared he'd be taken up for stealing it.
"I think you're right, old son," he said, similarly taken aback.
I said, "Well, I never knew the pollis shut."
"D'y'think they're worried somebody's gona break in and steal your Grandad?" he asked.

We walked round the building and every entrance was secured. When we returned to the front door Uncle Freddie found a bell marked NIGHT BELL.
"Right," he decided, "Hate to disturb their beauty sleep, but here goes."
He heaved on the bell and somewhere inside the fortress we heard its muffled chiming.
"Mebbes we should come back in the morning?" I suggested.
"Too late, old son," said Uncle Freddie, ear to the door, "I hear the distant tread of a pair of number twelves approaching."
The door duly creaked open and the fat policeman said, "Wha'd'y'want?"
Uncle Freddie stared at him and said, cautiously, "We have the right door? This is the pollis station?"
The constable held the door firmly, sniffed and admitted, "That's right, sir. This is the pollis station. Wha'd'y'want?"
"Well, can wi come in?" asked Uncle Freddie, puzzled.
The fat policeman sighed and made to close the door.
"Let it wait 'til the morn, eh? We're busy."
Uncle Freddie seized the edge of the door and said, "Busy?"
The fat policeman decided not to wrestle Uncle Freddie for the door, but suggested, "Look, sir," with an unhealthy emphasis on the 'sir', "I don't think you know much about the pollis?"
Uncle Freddie admitted, "I've always kept me distance," and released his grip on the door.
"Exactly," said the stout representative of the law, "Most we invite in has to be dragged in."
He made to close the door, but I said, "It's about my Grandad. He hasn't come back."
"Lost and Found is only open office hours, son," said the kindly constable.
"The old gentleman you took in this morning," suggested Uncle Freddie, "For singing in the street?"
The door was opened wider.
"Davie Ferguson! Now the mantle's lit!," said our obstructive gendarme, "Singing in the street. Causing an affray. That's a serious offence."
"Singing in the street," argued Uncle Freddie, "I don't deny. But a bit ower old for causing an affray, surely?"
"You're wrong there," said the majesty of the law, sternly, "Inspector Elliott had his whistle rammed up his nose. And he was bitten on the buttock."
"That was a dog!" I cried indignantly, "Not my Grandad's fault."
"Well, you can imagine the Inspector wasn't any too pleased," said the constable.
"Can we have him back, please?" I pleaded.

"Your Granda's all right," said the fat policeman, "No worry there. Right as rain."
He made to close the door again, but Uncle Freddie held it in a vicelike grip.
"Well, then," he asked, most reasonably, "Can I not sign some chittee and take him off your hands?"
The constable shook his head gravely.
"Sorry, sir. We cannot release him yet."
Uncle Freddie was bewildered.
"You're treating this very serious," he said, "What's the charge?"
"There's no charge," the fat policeman admitted, " It's by private invitation."
He tried to close the door, but Uncle Freddie didn't yield an inch.
"Wha'd'y'mean 'private invitation'?" my amiable uncle asked, "What's going on?"
The constable gave up the struggle for the door.
"The old gentleman's doing a smoker for us," he admitted.
"A concert?" we cried in chorus.
"Big do. The Superintendent's here. And the Chief Constable. Ladies and all."
Uncle Freddie and I gazed at one another in astonishment.
"Davie's singing for yi?" asked Uncle Freddie.
In a voice warm with admiration, the fat policeman said, "Aw, man, lovely voice the old gent's got," and looking at our stupefied faces, "I suppose you'd better come in."
He released the door and we entered the hallway.
"Yi can stand at the back," he said generously, "But don't let the nobs see yi. Specially not Elliott."
"Is the whistle still up his nose?" I enquired.
"Something definitely got up his nose," our friendly gendarme replied.
And so we stood in the back of the little drill hall and I wept to myself as my grandfather sang the Rose of Tralee, a song he often sang for my mother, expressing a love that somehow I could never ever make plain. I didn't dare look up at Uncle Freddie, but held tightly to his hand which wrung mine like a dish clout.

When Grandad finished singing Uncle Freddie blew his nose loudly while everybody clapped and shouted encore and I scrubbed my eyes on my gansey sleeve because of the bright lights. They force the gangsters to look into the bright lights when they give them the third degree. Did you know that? It makes their eyes water and they have to tell the truth then.

Since the day Uncle Freddie got his job as a tram conductor, a dazzling figure in his smart uniform with shining buttons and jaunty cap, I had become a fixture on the old Jarrow Number Two. This was the tram piloted punctiliously by Gasser Gillespie, tickets trimmed and pennies pouched by my Uncle Freddie who was rewarded with the job, you will remember, for snatching a falling baby out of thin air.

The Jarrow & District Electric Traction Company ran its maroon and white open-top trams emblazoned with the magnet and the wheel from Western Road past Palmers, down Ormonde Street, Staple Road, the High Street, out from Jarrowtown down Church Bank and past St. Paul's Church where Bede used to live, but that was before the trams. On past the Swinburne Street depot into Jarrow Road where the tramway ran under Tyne Dock arches and you could almost touch the sooty, slimy roof. From there the trams ran on through South Shields to the Pier Head, down to the glorious sands of Shields. That's what we used to sing: Shields sands, Shields sands, best sands in all the land!

One day when we were sitting at the Pier Head waiting to make the return run, enjoying the sea breezes, throwing a stick across the sands for a daft dog, I unburdened myself of my problem. The purchase of a proper present for my mother's birthday weighed even more heavily upon my shoulders than the knowledge that Uncle Freddie didn't insist on all his passengers buying tickets. He never charged Jimmy Hunter who left his legs in Flanders and he'd wink at old wives and pretend he couldn't see their penny. He was puzzled I hadn't mentioned it before and looked hurt that I couldn't share my worry with him.
"You should've told me, old son," he said and dived his hand into his pocket.
"Here," he said and brought out a sixpence, "Here ya, old sausage."
"Sixpence?" I gasped, "A whole sixpence?"
He smiled and said, "Buy something nice for your Mam. She deserves it."
"But I didn't expect you to give me money," I explained.
"I'm not giving you money. How long have you been working as assistant conductor on the trams now?"
"Six weeks," I answered.
"Then I've been a bit remiss with your lying-on money," he admitted.
"Don't know what you mean."
The panting dog arrived in a flurry of sand and dropped the stick for Uncle Freddie to throw again. He threw the stick and the dog, barking joyfully, hared after it.
"When yi get taken on yi work the first two weeks and only get paid for one," he explained.
That didn't make much sense to me.

"How'd yi manage on one week's money?"
Uncle Freddie cleaned his hands in the sand.
"Very badly," he said.
"But when d'y'get the lying-on money?" I asked puzzled by the intricacies of international finance.
"When you're paid off," explained Uncle Freddie, "Then you're so grateful to get your money yi don't notice yi've lost your job."
"It sounds a very peculiar system to me," I said, "And very unfair."
The mad dog crashed into our legs, delirious at having found somebody willing to throw sticks. Uncle Freddie took the stick and threw it in a high curving arc. The dog ran blindly towards the sea.
"It's called capitalism," my Uncle Freddie explained, "They throw the stick. We run after it."
The dog had lost sight of the flight of the stick and was ranging madly across the sands of Shields. Uncle Freddie dusted sand off his hands and said, "Let's get back before Gasser thinks we've jumped ship."
On the way back to the tram I asked him, "Does this mean yi don't want me on the tram any more?"
He laughed and shook my shoulder.
"Never!" he said, "This is what we call compassionate circumstances."
"What does that mean?"
"It means your Mam deserves a decent birthday present."
We swung aboard our tram, Uncle Freddie rang the bell for Gasser to proceed and I went upstairs to ride the chariot back to Jarrow while Uncle Freddie sold tickets only to selected passengers.

So there I was worrying myself about nothing: how to acquire the spondoolicks to buy my mother the most wonderful birthday present ever, which gift, thanks to Uncle Freddie's generosity, would now be supplied by Dando's who had brooches with all the names on. They were real mother of pearl with gold pins. Price fivepence three farthings. Uncle Freddie had solved my problem with one movement of his calloused paw, in and out of his pocket. All even-steven in a twinkling. It was clear that God was in Hebburn and all was plain sailing in my world. Until the serpent appeared in Eden, a sneaky snake by the name of Norman Richardson.

I was Norman's best friend. To be honest I was Norman Richardson's one and only friend. His mother wouldn't let him play in the street. He had to have friends in to play and nobody could put up with Norman for very long even if his mother dispensed Little Gem biscuits and Robinson's Barley Water with a liberal hand. Norman had no father. He had, Mrs. Richardson said, perished in the Deep. Oddly enough that's what they called the old Pacific pub on Western Road, Jarrow. The Deep. Many a good man sank there without trace.

If he didn't have a father, Norman certainly had a superfluity of uncles, sometimes two or three different ones in a week. They would appear and stay for a night, a weekend, a week or even a month if their ship was held back for any reason. Norman was never short of sixpences or Little Gem biscuits or Robinson's Barley Water. What he lacked were friends. Nobody wanted to play with Norman even though he had all the toys nobody else possessed. Mrs. Richardson would accept any excuse just to see me on the step. To have somebody come in and play with Norman. She was a trier was Mrs. Richardson. She certainly tried hard for Norman.

I admit I wasn't a true friend to Norman. What I wanted from him was access to his Encyclopaedias, volumes one to twelve. What I valued above all else he didn't give a second glance, what I could spend all day immersed therein, he never opened. His mother wasn't so stupid that she didn't understand why I was there, but she loved her son and any companionship was better than none. However, I'd hardly be across her doorstep before she'd grab me to insist I allowed her to wash my face and hands with her lavender soap and flannel. It was an indignity not lightly to be borne. Since my mother had provided me with my own set of Encyclopaedias I had somewhat neglected Norman. However, with sixpence in my pocket, a hunger for Little Gem Biscuits and Barley Water I had an ever-acceptable excuse for knocking on Mrs. Richardson's front door. I was even prepared for the martyrdom of face cloth and lavender soap. I went round to Norman's house.

"I had a good wash before I came," I explained, "Yi can still smell the soap."
"That's as may be," Mrs. Richardson exclaimed, "We have to be as clean as a whistle before we open those excitelopeadias. His Dadda would expect it. A good book, he would say, is - now what was it he used to say?"
She seized my right hand and scrubbed it briskly with a nail brush.
I offered, "A good book is the lifeblood of a master spirit?"
"Oh, no," said Mrs. Richardson, "He never indulged in crudities. Where do you learn such language, Lecky Fergie? Lifeblood indeed!"
I explained, "It's written in the front of lots of books."
"That's why I won't let Norman go near that library. You never know where those books have been. The bedbugs use them like the trams. I've seen old men go in there you wouldn't touch with a clothes prop. What do they want with

reading at their age? They ought to be ashamed of themselves."
Having skinned my right hand she started as briskly on my left.
"Norman has nice hands," she remarked, "So did his Dadda. Lovely hands. He's going to learn the pianoforte, y'know."
"How can he if he's dead?" I asked, intrigued at the notion of a post-mortem pianist.
"Norman is. When we get a pianoforte. Or even an accordion."
"Accordion to what you can afford," I riposted merrily.
Mrs. Richardson rapped my knuckles with the nail brush.
"I'll be the best judge of that, Mister Nosey Parker," she remarked acidly.
"It was a joke," I explained, "It was in a comic."
"Comics!" cried Mrs. Richardson and the nail brush moved at such a pace Early Man would've been proud of her efforts as a fire raiser, "I won't have comics in the house. His Dadda said that. I won't have comics in this house. He scrumpled it up, stuffed it down the bowl and pulled the string. It flooded the yard it wouldn't go down. There you are, he said, that's comics for you!"
She was a sad, lonely woman, putting on a bold face, who endured the life she did for her son. Perhaps she just wanted somebody to talk to and nobody would stand still long enough. I shouldn't imagine any of the numerous Uncles ever bothered to listen to her. So she pinned me to her draining board and talked at me. I hated that lavender soap, but I endured it for the love of Little Gem biscuits and Robinson's Barley Water. She must've saved my mother a fortune in soap.
She dried my face despite my protests, combed my hair, gave me the once-over and said, "I'm glad you've come to play with Norman. He's been a bit down since you were last here. You're quite a stranger."
I told lies to Mrs. Richardson without a single qualm of conscience just to keep in practice.
"Our dog's had rabies," I explained, "I'm the only one he'd sit with. He was biting everybody else. So I had to stay home and look after him. He's dead now so I can come out to play."
"Oh, dear," said Mrs. Richardson, a gentle soul easily moved to tears, "I am sorry to hear that. Did he suffer much?"
"He never complained, " I said, sadly, "He just gave one last bark and dropped his bone. Then he fell dead. The funeral's Thursday. If you want to come."
"Norman's had a little cough," she said thoughtfully, "But I don't think it's the rabies."
She brightened up and said, "I know he'll be pleased to see you. I think you're what his Dadda would've called a Good Influence."
She moved to go to the foot of the stairs to call Norman from his bedroom where

he spent the greater part of his life, but turned and said, "I remember now. He would say, would his Dadda, 'a good book makes for a canny sit, but only the Bible makes holy smoke.' That's what he'd say, Lecky."
"It doesn't make sense," I replied.
"Not to you," she replied, with a dismissive laugh, "Norman's Dadda was an educated man."

We were playing quite happily on the new carpet, well-supplied with Little Gem biscuits and Robinson's Barley Water while Mrs. Richardson sat in her chair reading a magazine and idly eating liqueur chocolates when Norman cried out, "I've found a sixpence on the floor, Mammy!"
Norman had used the Encyclopaedias to build the castle wall so that while he was merrily bombarding the fortress with his toy cannons I was engaged in reading the West Gate.
Alarm pierced me as a misplaced javelin. I dived my hand into my pocket. My precious sixpence was no longer in residence.
"Well, who's a lucky boy then?" chuckled his mother fondly.
"That's mine!" I cried, "That's my sixpence!"
"Oh?" Mrs. Richardson enquired, "And whose floral tufted at three and ninepence per yard, is it, may I ask?"
As I struggled to find the connection between my sixpence coming adrift and the ownership of the carpet, Norman petitioned his mother with, "Can I keep it, Mammy?"
"Of course, you can, pet," said his mother, "If you'll give your Mammy a big kiss."
While Norman slobbered over his mother I went through all my pockets lest I should be mistaken. I was not. My sixpence had vanished.
"That'll be your Uncle Wally," said Mrs. Richardson, giggling like a schoolgirl, "The first thing he did when he came in and saw the new carpet was he had to have a lie down on it."
"It's not his, " I insisted, "It's mine. It fell out of my pocket."
Mrs. Richardson regarded me severely.
"Oh, Lecky Fergie," she said sorrowfully, "I blush for you. How can you say that?"
"Because it's true," I insisted, "It is my sixpence!"
Norman stuck out his tongue at me and said, "It's my sixpence. I found it. Finder's keeper's."
"Loser's weepers, " finished Mrs. Richardson, "That's the law."
"No, it's not!" I protested.
"Though I doubt it'll bother Wally," she reminisced, "I've seen him leave as

much as thruppence wet change on the bar. 'If you think I'm putting that in me pocket,' he says. First time I couldn't believe it. I just wrap it in a hanky now."
I pleaded, desperate to be heard and believed.
"God's Holy Honour, it's my sixpence, Mrs. Richardson! It's come out of my pocket!"
She regarded me with the sympathy mingled with amusement with which one might regard a drunken man stepping short of the ferry and falling headlong into the water.
She explained, "Hurworth Place, you're just not sixpenny people, Lecky. Now Norman's well acquainted with sixpences. Aren't you, Norman, pet? If it's not Uncle Wally being free-handed it's his Uncle Cyril. He cannot be bothered with anything less than half a crown."
I was on my knees before her chair.
"Uncle Freddie gave it to me," I pleaded, "For our Mam's birthday. To buy her a present."
Mrs. Richardson closed the lid of the liqueur chocolates and leaned forward to breathe a bouquet of chocolate and brandy over me. She said, as sternly as her angel bow mouth could manage, "I don't know why you're persisting, Lecky Fergie. I'm very disappointed in you. I only hope God's not listening."
She leaned back in her chair as if imploring the Almighty to be as forgiving as she was and not smite me with a misplaced thunderbolt that might singe her new carpet.
Searching wildly for any handhold, I cried, "I know what's on my sixpence. It says Georgius Vee. Dee Gra. Brit Omnee. Rex. Fid Def. Ind Imp."
Mrs. Richardson sat up and said, "Let's see it, Norman, pet."
Reluctantly her pet handed over the coin and I watched the wavering of Mrs. Richardson's lips as she read the inscription.
"Well," she said, "If it does I don't see how that helps with indemnification."
Inspired by desperation, I explained, "Fid Def is Latin for Freddie Dean."
Norman snorted, but his mother said, "Well, I never knew that!"
"Brit Omnee is British Trams," I cried, stepping even further out onto thin ice, "Omnibus, yi see?"
I glared at Norman daring him to contradict me.
Mrs. Richardson asked, "What about Rex?"
I was way out on the ice now executing a brilliant figure of eight.
"That's our dog's name," I explained.
"You haven't got a dog," said Norman.
"Not now," I said, sadly, "He's dead. But his name's still alive."
Mrs. Richardson nodded gravely.
"Ask him about Dee Gra, Mammy," suggested Norman, spitefully.

I completed a triple jump and spin.
"Donated in Gratitude," I said, "For helping on the tram"
Norman said, "What about Ind Imp then?"
His face said, Got you there!
"Individually imprinted," I answered and stuck my tongue out at him.
Mrs. Richardson said, reluctantly, "It looks like he's right, Norman, pet."
From the centre of the ice I bowed and acknowledged the applause of the admiring crowd on the banks of the lake.
Norman jumped up with an unusual display of energy.
"He's making it up, Mammy," he cried plaintively, "I know he is!"
"Well, I don't know what to do for the best," said Mrs. Richardson with a heartfelt sigh.
"Please, Mrs. Richardson," I begged her, "It is my sixpence."
"Then," she said, "Seeing as Norman found it for you, you must share it with him."
I fell through the ice into the pitch black icy depths and drowned. I gaped at Mrs. Richardson.
"But it's for my mother's birthday present!"
Mrs. Richardson regarded me with scornful amusement.
"What would your Mammy want a birthday for at her time of life? In Hurworth Place? No, it's only fair you treat Norman to the pictures."
Norman said, "Shirley Temple's on at the Kino, Lecky."
Ah, alas, the treacherous serpent that once betrayed Adam had bitten me in the leg!
"Shirley Temple?" I cried, overcome by a vision of that sweet moppet, "What's she in?"
"Wee Willie Winkie," Norman said and I was lost.
When I hesitated, torn between wild horses, Mrs. Richardson suggested, slyly, "Besides Norman'll be having any amount of sixpences at the weekend. When Uncle Harold comes to stay. You'll give a sixpence to Lecky, won't you, pet?"
"Do I have to?" he sulked.
"Just to please Mammy?" she cajoled.
He made a motion of the head that might have suggested agreement or constipation.
"If you're sure," I said.
"Sure as sure, Lecky," Mrs. Richardson coaxed me, "You shall have your sixpence. Ooh, I wish I was going with you! Shirley's one of my very own favourites."
"Why don't you come?" I suggested gallantly, "If you've got Uncle Wally's wet change. I expect it's dry now."

"I'd love to, Lecky, pet," said Mrs. Richardson, "Only Uncle Terry said he'd drop in this afternoon to see about sauce pans. Would you believe that woman hides his collar studs so's he cannot get out? Mind, she's been under the doctor since Easter, but her ears are still very queer."
I said, "Our Mam's worried about my ears, but I don't want that."
"Don't want what, pet?" she smiled.
"The doctor sitting on them," I responded.
Mrs. Richardson opened her liqueur chocolates and chose an orange Armagnac. "D'y'know what, Lecky?" she said, popping the chocolate gobbet into her crimson-stained gob, "Sometimes I feel really sorry for your Mam."
In this sad fashion did I betray my mother and Uncle Freddie for love of the golden-haired moppet, sweetheart of all the world, the incomparable Shirley Temple.

As any devout Moslem bows to Mecca so was the Kino my true spiritual home. Wild horses and iron chains could not have kept me away from the tuppenny rush, otherwise known as the Saturday matinee, but with 'Continual Performance' I always lingered as late as I dared, reluctant to emerge blinking into daylight or twilight through the musty velvet curtains smothering the entrances to my Elysium. We always demanded and enjoyed a full programme which included the newsreel, an advert for a garage that seemingly specialised in antique automobiles and engineers with bushy moustaches and bowler hats, the COMING-SHORTLY-s, the cartoon, the short, the B picture and the Big Picture.

Any entomologist would doubtless have found the Kino a happy hunting ground, but the manager, Mr. McKie, complete with pipe, Clark Gable moustache and stern expression, patrolled the aisles at regular intervals, spraying the seething rows with a busy Flit gun. Whether this was to reduce the insect population or the smell of unwashed bodies we cared not. We regarded it as a rare treat, breathing deeply of the carbolic vapour floating in the projector beam.

Scarcely had Norman and I settled down, under the benign spray of the Flit gun, with our ha'penny dips, MacAtominey's-Meal-In-A-Moment, halfway to our gobs when I realised that the COMING SHORTLY I was looking at was my idol, Shirley Temple, nattily attired as a wee Scottish soldier, complete with sporran, singing and saluting in a scene from WEE WILLIE WINKIE. I turned to Norman, my face shining with bewilderment and pork fat, to cry, "Shirley's not on today! She's COMING SHORTLY! You've got it wrong, Norman!"
He ignored me, his gaze apparently devoted to Shirley's antics.

"Norman!" I hissed, "She's not on 'til next week!"
As he continued to ignore me, munching on his dip, I realised that treacherous Norman had cheated me once again.
"You knew!" I hissed, "You knew, didn't you?"
I punched him on the shoulder and he dropped his dip.
"Now see what you've done!" he cried.
When he scrabbled on the floor for his dip I followed him down to punch him again, but I didn't enjoy it. Guilt consumed me.
"I'd never have spent Our Mam's sixpence else," I said sadly.
Norman struggling to find his dip and having his hands kicked and stamped on by complaining cinema-goers in front of us, retorted, "It wasn't your sixpence. I found it. It was mine."
"You sneaky pig, Norman," I hissed, "You know I worship Shirley Temple!"
Retrieving his dilapidated dip, Norman returned to his seat and I followed suit.
"Well, we're going to see a proper picture instead," he said, defiantly, "Not one for lasses who want to be nurses."
"What're we going to see?" I asked.
"The Old Dark House," said Norman, and settled into his seat with a smug smile to chew on his dusty dip.
When the young couple driving through the storm sought shelter at the old dark house and the door opened to reveal Ernest Thesiger's skull-like face in the flickering gloom I knew it was the wrong decision: for them and for Norman and me.
By the time Eva Moore as the old woman had put in a few cackles and dark fore-bodings I was in a state of silent hysteria and Norman was sitting very still with the remains of his dip frozen in his face.
When something started laughing in the darkness upstairs I knew I couldn't run away because my legs wouldn't hold me up. My dip slipped from my grasp and I never saw it again.
When the hand appeared on the banisters and began to creep downwards that was the finish of us. Our bladders filled up like the hull of the Titanic and our knees turned to water. Norman hid his head in his gansey and crouched on the floor, whimpering. I couldn't take my terrified eyes from the screen. There was no way we were ever going to run the gauntlet of the musty curtains at the exit where Ernest Thesiger was lying in wait. We were trapped in Continuous Performance.

Finally my father came to drag us out of the Kino, but there was no rational explanation I could offer that he might understand. How could I explain to this iron man that I had been too afraid of shadows to leave my seat? Despite my mother and Auntie Bella's pleas my father took his belt to me. At least I gave no one the satisfaction of tears which only confirmed to my father that I was without decent feeling or concern for anyone but myself. I lay in my bed and wept silently, not because I'd had a thrashing, but because my father was right. I was without feeling or concern for anything but my own selfish satisfaction. There was no sixpence and no present for my mother's birthday. When my father's anger had finally subsided and he had gone late to his work, losing half a shift, my mother came to comfort me, but I stubbornly pretended to be asleep. She left me, as comfortless and saddened as I was myself and went to her lonely bed.

On Friday night there was a big row at Norman Richardson's house. Two of his uncles turned up at the same time and the police had to come and drag them apart. When I called round on Saturday to be recompensed for my folly there were no silver sixpences to spare. Mrs. Richardson had retired to her bed for the weekend on doctor's orders to restore her nervous composure. So I gave Norman a good punching to improve his nervous composure, robbed the biscuit tin of Little Gems and ran away from home to be a cabin boy on a schooner trading in the South Seas. The first problem was to transport myself to the southern hemisphere.

Tyne Dock Gate was shut by the time I walked through from Jarrow and I couldn't make the watchmen hear me. A mournful fog had crept over the familiar river, erasing the known world. When like an illuminated bumble bee, a tram rolled through the Arches and a familiar figure climbed down to reverse the boom, I didn't know whether to feel relieved or guilty.

Uncle Freddie said, "Lecky? What're you doing here this time of night?"
"I'm running away," I said.
"Are you now?" he said, thoughtfully. I followed him as he reversed the boom.
"I'm going to be a cabin boy."
"There's nobody signing on cabin boys this time of night," he responded, without batting an eyelid.
I should've realised there'd be an acknowledged etiquette in such matters.
"Is there a special time?" I enquired anxiously.
"Twelve noon," said my uncle, "On the dot."
"I cannot go home," I said.
He regarded me soberly.
"I heard about you and your Dad," he said, and rang his ticket machine twice,

"Why don't you stay overnight with your Auntie Bella?"
I shook my head sadly.
"I cannot go back."
Uncle Freddie said, "I cannot leave the tram, old son."
"Don't worry about me," I reassured him, "I'll be all right."
Uncle Freddie hesitated to swing aboard the tram.
"Tell you what, old sausage," he suggested, "You go to Annie Stayshere's fried fish shop up Hudson Street."
"Why?" I asked.
"There's many a sea captain drops in there for a fish supper," he declared, "Besides it'll be handy in the morning for the Dock gate. You'd be first in line for cabin boys."
"She doesn't know me," I objected.
My uncle took me by the arm.
"Tell her I sent you," he insisted, "Tell her you're in a pickle. She'll give yi a shakedown. Promise me?"
The fog was swirling about us, eavesdropping on our conversation and the old Jarrow Number Two was melting away.
I agreed reluctantly, saying, "All right, but I'm still running away to sea."
"Nobody's trying to stop you," he declared, "We'll find you a grand ship in the morn. How many funnels d'y'fancy?"
He swung aboard the tram and rang the bell. The tram began to move.
"Where's the chip shop, Uncle Freddie?" I cried.
"Follow your nose," he cried as the lighted bumble bee vanished into the abyss of the Arches.

I had no problem finding the fish shop, but like everywhere else on that fog-wrapped night it was snugly secured. I began to understand how cats with dewy fur feel sleeping on doorsteps, waiting for the world to begin again. I could see there was a light through the back and so I kept on banging at the door until a presence blotted out the inner light and approached the door.
"Go away," said a woman's voice, "Shop is shut."
Through the letter box I said, "I don't want fish and chips."
"Come back tomorrow," said the woman and began to move away.
Desperately I cried, "My Uncle Freddie said to come."
"Freddie Dean?" said the woman's voice.
There was a long silence and then the woman unlocked the door and withdrew the bolt. There was the ping of the shop bell as she cautiously opened the door a few inches and peered out at me.

"Do I know you, darling?" she said in a voice, a foreign voice, that reminded me of Aladdin's wicked Uncle.
"He said to tell you I'm in a pickle."
The woman behind the door laughed like a man.
"You look very small to be a pickle. What have you done?" she said sternly.
"I've run away to be a cabin boy," I admitted, "I've got to sign on the dot tomorrow."

The door opened wide and my new friend said, "Come on in, darling. Come inside before the fog gets in your bones."
Smiling in the doorway was the fattest woman I have ever seen. Perhaps she was the fattest woman in all the world? She had arms like horse flanks and a tiny rosebud mouth in a face bigger than the harvest moon. Come inside? Not a mouse could've passed her on the step.

"Don't be shy!" said Annie Stayshere, "All the warm is walking out and the cold is running in!"
I squeezed past her, pressed against the warm comfort of her stomach, through the dark shop and into the furnace of her kitchen, steeped in meat dripping and fish batter. A fire blazed in the chimney, big enough to melt an iceberg, and Annie's chair was still rocking, nodding patiently, awaiting her ponderous return.
"It's very kind of you to take me in like this, Mrs. Stayshere," I recited politely, "I'll try not to be any trouble. I'll be gone in the morning as soon as I can get a ship. I expect I'll send you a postcard from Tierra del Fuego or even Fray Bentos if you like."
Annie laughed outrageously and the mountain rumbled its reply.
"My darling," she said, "Freddie Dean's name is good here. He has been a fine friend to me. Take off that wet coat and come to the fire."
If I had approached the fire any closer I would've turned to toast, but I took off my coat and settled on a wooden stool as she bid me. She looked at me smiling and said, "I think Freddie is right. You are a pickle. Good. I am expert in pickles."

Annie Stayshere had the biggest pickle jar in Shields on her shop counter and Mams would warn their bairns not to dip into Annie's jar lest they fall in and vinaigrette themselves.

Annie settled herself into her chair, saying, "What shall I call you?"
"I would prefer to be anonymous, thank you, Mrs. Stayshere," I replied.
She sighed and answered, "Once upon a time. In another world. My father

owned paintings by Anonymous Bosch. I think that was his name. Would he be any relation, darling?"

"My Uncle George is a painter," I suggested helpfully, "In Birkenhead. He had to leave Jarrow because."
"Because what?" asked Annie.
"I don't know," I said, "That's all they say if you ask. Because."
The fat woman sighed deeply and the kitchen resonated in harmony.
"I too had to leave. Because," she said, "But no matter. I am Annie Stayshere, the biggest tub afloat in Tyne Dock."
The woman laughed loudly, but I was deeply discomforted.
"I don't think you're that fat, Mrs. Stayshere," I responded gallantly.
The good lady rocked forward and slapped me on the knee.
"Bless you, darling!" she cried, "Your Mama has raised a gentleman. But tell the truth and shame the Devil! Annie Stayshere is fatter far than any three ladies in Hudson Street, Mister Anonymous!"
She wore a muffler about her neck despite the heat of the kitchen and a man's cap was perched on her head. She had blue eyes, hair the colour of straw and at least three chins. A black balloon of a cat yawned from the overcrowded sideboard, staring at us with languid amber eyes.
She was such a kindly woman I could travel no further incognito.
"My real name's Alexander," I said, "Not Anonymous."
Annie Stayshere beamed like the sun emerging from summer clouds, saying, "Ah! Aleksandr! Now that is a royal name!"
"They only say Alexander when I've done something wrong," I explained, sadly.
"And you have done something wrong?" the astute lady asked, "That is why you wish to be a cabin boy?"
I said, "Everything's awful."
She clucked like a broody hen and said, "Tell me about it, darling," in such a sympathetic tone that I poured out my heart to her and she listened, clucking, laughing, sighing, crying. I felt heart's ache begin to melt away.
"What do you think I should do?" I asked.
She smiled and patted my cheek, saying, "You will know what to do, Aleksandr."
"When?"
"I forget my manners," said Annie briskly, "You must be as hungry as a horse-fly!"
"I could eat a horse!" I cried.
"No, no!" she corrected me, "We will have fried fish and chips. I have some cod pieces I was saving for the cat."

While she prepared and fried the largest pieces of cod I had ever seen we talked and as I had opened my heart to her so Annie Stayshere opened her generous heart to me.
"I was a refugee," said Annie, "You know what refugee is?"
"You escaped from the War."
"When I came to Tyne Dock I had no boots," she said, nodding sagely as she dipped the white fish flesh into a creamy golden batter.
I laughed, and said, disbelievingly, "No boots?"
She looked at me sternly and said, "Oh, the captain of the boat he would have given me boots, but I said, no, thank you, Mister Captain!"
I wondered, "Wasn't it cold?"
She placed the fish into the applause of the hot fat.
"I had rags wrapped round my feet and legs," she explained, "Like our Russian peasants. Such people have no boots."
I remembered the summery pictures in the Encyclopaedia of pleasant peasants and musical moujiks.
"But I thought they were always laughing and dancing about?"
Annie stirred the fish to swim faster and said, sadly, "There is not a lot to laugh about in our poor Russia."
I dared to ask, "Was it not a bit? Cheesy?"
Annie Stayshere lifted out the most glorious golden fish and added it to the log-jam of chips on my plate. She laughed aloud and said, "Exactly! Cheesy! Stinky woman, they say. They keep their distance."
We sat at her table like friends of long standing. We drank great mugs of black tea and ate the finest fish and chips that I have ever tasted in my lifetime.
With a perky chip perched on my fork as Groucho would've posed with a cigar I asked, "But why? If the captain would've given you boots?"
"Aha, Aleksandr!" she cried, her rosebud mouth glistening with grease, "A mystery, heh? Why would a poor woman refuse such kindness?"
I pondered the puzzle and responded, "Because you hadn't washed your feet and didn't want them to see."
Annie cut and ate a last sliver of succulent codfish before putting down her knife and fork. She wiped her mouth daintily on the cat's tail and said, "If I were to tell you that what fortune I had left I carried out from Russia between my toes and round my ankles, would you believe me, Sasha?"
My eyes opened like daisies drawn to the sun. My heart was beating like Mrs. Chamberlain's baby, George, falling down their back stairs, bump, bump, bumpity-bump!
"Yes!" I cried, "Yes, I would believe you!"
Annie Stayshere reached across and caught my hand.

"And that I am the sole surviving daughter of the last Czar of All the Russias?"
"Oh, golly!" I cried, breathless. My heart had stopped as abruptly as baby George on hitting the bottom passage wall.
Annie Stayshere reached to take both my hands. The chip fell off my fork.
"It is a secret to be shared between us, Sasha," she whispered, "A secret to be shared until death!"
"I swear," I cried, "Unto death. I've done it before. To save my eyeballs."
Annie released my hands and sat back in her chair.
"When I landed in Tyne Dock," said Annie Stayshere, her eyes clouding with memory, "I walked to a pawnshop in Laygate and there I stripped off my leg wrappings. Despite the protests of the shopman!"
"I didn't know they were that particular in Laygate," I responded. Casually I speared my last chip and transferred it to my mouth.
Annie Stayshere laughed aloud.
"I fear it was not so much his nose I offended as his modesty, my darling!" said she, "But when he saw what my wrappings had concealed he was eager enough to lock the shop door."
"And?" I cried.
My hostess hesitated, looked behind her for eavesdroppers, and then said, "Between the toes of each foot I carried the last of the Romanoff diamonds."
When I retrieved my breath from whence it had gone whistling away, I said, "Diamonds? Real diamonds?"
Annie Stayshere sighed deeply, shook her head and swallowed a large mouthful of black tea.
"Sadly all that was left of my father, the Czar Nicholas's family fortune, my darling Sasha," she sighed, "Where once we had diamonds by the bucketful I had, but a handful. Where once I had a forest of gold chains only what I wrapped about my ankles."
"In the Encyclopaedia," I told the last of the Romanov princesses, "it says the fabulous fortune of the Romanovs has never been traced, but the Bolshevik secret police will never relinquish the scent."
Surprised, the Princess Annie Stayshere said, "You are well-read, Aleksandr!"
"Our Dad says it's a pity I cannot do something more useful," I admitted, "But go on! What happened in the pawnbroker's in Laygate?"
Annie Stayshere finished her tea and set down her mug with an approving thump.
"I made a bargain with Alprovich the pawnbroker, a Jew, but a good man and a true Russian, that he should have one diamond for himself and sell one for me. To buy the fish shop. The rest he should safeguard until the great day comes."
"What great day?" I asked.

There came over that amiable countenance such an expression of longing, of loneliness, of loss that I found it almost unbearable to look at her.
"When the nightmare is over, Sasha," she answered wistfully, "When I go home to claim my own. That blessed day, Aleksandr, when Holy Mother Russia is free. And I can go home again."
I couldn't help the tears that flowed from my eyes, but I saw her eyes were moist too. Until that moment I never knew that grown-up hearts could ache for home. I didn't know it was a lifelong, ineradicable, fatal disease, this longing to go home. We sat, the would-be cabin boy and the last princess of Russia in that furnace of a kitchen and the magic word HOME hung in the air stronger even than the scent of fish and chips.
I blew my nose and said, "I hope you do go home one day, Mrs. Stayshere."
"Thank you," she said, "And I hope you too will find your heart's desire one day."
"But I thought," I persisted, "That all the Royal family were murdered?"
Annie Stayshere sighed, and answered, "Yes. That is true."
"What about you then?"
"They left me for dead on the cellar floor," she answered and pulled away the muffler from around her neck. By the light of the fire I saw the puckered lips of scars about to whistle the Dead March from Saul. Hurriedly she hid her savage souvenir.
"Forgive me," said she, "I forget you are a child."
"Necks don't scare me," I said, "I've seen the Old Dark House. How did you escape?"
Annie Stayshere looked at me with a measured glance.
"Tell me," she asked, "Next to a good Russian, who are the finest, the bravest people on God's earth?"
I shook my head.
"I don't know."
"Geordies are the best in all the world, my darling. Geordies are very Russian," she cried.
I told her, "Granny Fergie says Geordies are God's bad lads."
Annie Stayshere laughed, took my hand and rising we went back to sit by the fire, leaving the cat to wash the dishes.
"When I met my Geordies," said Annie, "the Bolsheviks were shelling the town and the people were running away. I shout out to these sailors my name. Anastasia, I cry out, Anastasia!"
In my head I saw the dying town, the buildings falling, the grim artillerymen, the fleeing townsfolk, and this girl with eyes of cerulean blue and hair like golden corn, bewildered, lost, wounded.

"But my Geordies they tell me, 'Don't be so daft, lass! Anna stays here? Anna's not staying here! She's coming with Geordie! That's what she's doing! Haway with us, lass!"

It was one of those wonderful moments when the hair stands up on the back of your neck and you know there is much more to life than cowardice and fear, greed and avarice, lust and brutality. The flower of courage still blooms and its perfume colours the air brightly. The flag of human decency still flies from the beleaguered walls. Lift up your head and see! It flourishes yet in the battlestained air.

"Did they?" I cried, "Oh, how wonderful! I'm glad they were so brave!"

I clapped my hands with delight and Annie declared, "And so Annie did not stays there. So she is with Geordie in Tyne Dock. In her own fish shop. Here I am Annie Stayshere. Safe from Cheka. What is now called Ogpu. Safe from that monster in the Kremlin. Here with my Geordies!"

We sat in the happiest of silences until I said, gratefully, "That's a marvellous story, Mrs. Stayshere."

She shrugged her vast shoulders and said, "If you don't believe me, it is of no matter."

"But I do!" I cried, "I do believe you!"

Annie Stayshere shook her head, saying, "It is safer you don't believe me. These murderers have a long reach. Ogpu never sleeps. But I am wearing a good disguise."

I shivered with echoes of The Old Dark House raising ugly shadows in my head.

"Who's Mister Ogpu?" I whispered.

Annie sat as though turned to stone. Finally she said, "He is the secret policeman who murders at his master's command."

"This is England," I said in an attempt to reassure myself as much as Annie, "There's no one can touch you in England. This is a free country. You're safe here."

"Yes, you are right, Aleksandr, " she decided, "For all her faults she is a free country still," and rising from her chair, "But enough for tonight, darling. You can sleep on the couch. In the morning you can see what ships in Tyne Dock are short of cabin boys."

Annie Stayshere buried me under a mountain of blankets, counterpanes and quilts on the couch and kissed me good night.

I must've seemed surprised because she said to me, "That is what your Mama would do, would she not?" and my eyes filled with tears unbidden.

"Tomorrow," said Annie Stayshere, "will be a better day, Sasha. I promise," and with that she left me.

I fell into a deep sleep broken only by a frightening dream that Mr. Ogpu had come for me and was standing on my chest. I awoke in the early light to find that someone had climbed in the window and was standing on me.

I screamed and grabbed his leg and we both came crashing to the floor together. Flailing about on the floor I found the poker to my hand and I started hitting him with it as hard as I could. Sheer terror multiplied my muscles. He shouted at me to stop, but I didn't listen, beating at him again and again until I was free of the terror of the Old Dark House, free of the wretched self who had allowed himself to be duped into spending Our Mam's silver sixpence, free of the beating my father had inflicted upon me.

Then Annie Stayshere came down the stairs to seize my arm and Mister Ogpu staggered to his feet and fell out of the window by which he had entered. I stood trembling while Annie returned the poker to the fireplace.

"It was Ogpu, Mrs. Stayshere!" I cried.

"Ogpu?" she said.

"He tried to get in, but I bashed him for you," I explained, "It's a good job I was here."

To my surprise Annie Stayshere laughed and enveloped me within an elephantine embrace.

"Thank you, thank you, Aleksandr," she cried and hugged me so hard I couldn't breathe, "You have saved me. From a burglar, I think. Not Ogpu."

"No," I persisted, "I'm sure it was Ogpu. You could see by his face."

Annie Stayshere kissed me and hugged me again.

"If you say it was Ogpu," she decided, "I will not argue with you. You have been a brave boy and I am grateful."

"You don't have to be too grateful," I said, "I can't breathe when you hug me."

My affectionate captor released me, saying, "Now I have both embraced and embarrassed you. That is what women do as you will find out when you are older."

When Uncle Freddie arrived Annie Stayshere told him the whole story while I ate the most enormous breakfast of fried bread and cod roe washed down by half a gallon of strong black tea.

"Well then, old son, " said Uncle Freddie, "We'd best be getting down to the Dock to see what's on offer. D'y'fancy the South Seas and coral reefs? Or the North Atlantic and drifting pack ice?"

I looked at Annie Stayshere and said, "I've changed my mind, Uncle Freddie. I want to go home."

Annie smiled upon me, nodding, but saying nothing. Uncle Freddie said, "That's the ticket!"

When we moved to go Annie Stayshere said, "Wait. I have something for you, Aleksandr."
"I don't want a reward," I said, both hurt and puzzled.
"It's not for you," said Annie, "It's your mother's birthday today. Give her this."
Uncle Freddie and I both drew in a deep breath. It was a bright fire burning on a gold chain, a diamond such as Woolworth's did not sell.

My mother loved her gift, drawing it from hand to hand so that the fire might burn against her skin.
"Thank you very much, Lecky! It's a lovely birthday present," she said, showing off the jewel to the assembled company, my father, Bella, Freddie, Granny and Grandad Fergie, "You'd almost think it was real, wouldn't yi?"
Grudgingly my father said, "It wouldn't fool a proper jeweller for a minute."
"I don't want to fool anybody," my mother said.
"But it is real!" I cried, "It's one of the lost diamonds of the Romanovs!"
Everybody laughed and Auntie Bella said, "Eeh, what an imagination the bairn has!"
My grandfather lowered his beer glass to say in mild reproof, "He'll come to no harm o' that."
But my mother saw the hurt in my face and hugged me, saying, "If anybody ever asks me I shall say it's one of the Romanov diamonds."
"No, Our Mam!" I cried in alarm, "Don't do that! You mustn't do that!"
This provided our happy family with further amusement, but was very frustrating to me.
Granny Fergie said, "You cannot have it both ways, Lecky."
My mother said, "Is it all right if I say my son gave it to me for my birthday?"
"Yes," I said, "Say that when they ask you."
"And I shall never, ever part with it. Is that all right?" she enquired of me, smiling, "Never ever?"
I was overwhelmed with emotion.
"Now what's he bubbling about?" my father demanded, "Godfrey, it's worse than having a lass in the house!"
"I beg your pardon!" said Auntie Bella, indignantly.
"Granted!" my father said and my mother laughed again.
I wiped my eyes and held my mother's hand and saw Uncle Freddie was smiling at me. There was no need for words between us. My mother wore the Romanov diamond on Best Occasions for the rest of her life and took it with her when she departed. For my birthday I got a nurse's outfit, made by my mother, which served me right. So I added a wooden sword and the dustbin lid for a shield and went off on the Crusades instead.

"Right," said my father, "I take it everybody wants a piece of this cake? Even a certain somebody who didn't want it cut?"
To my astonishment my mother kissed my father, saying, "It's a beautiful cake, Davie. It seems such a shame to spoil it."
My father cut and sliced the cake, rapping my grandfather's knuckles with the knife blade as he reached to snaffle a fragment of icing. I marvelled he didn't cut his fingers off. He manoeuvred the first slice onto a plate for my mother and offered it to her, saying, "Here. Take this and eat it, Mary. Happy birthday! And many more!"
"Happy birthday!" we all chorused and Auntie Bella added, "Amen to that!"
I saw the shadow, the unspoken secret, pass between Auntie Bella and my Grandmother, but I didn't understand its significance. The hand I felt upon my shoulder was Uncle Freddie's, my constant loving friend.

But in my head now I am watching my father, clumsily offering his love in cake, almond paste and icing to my mother. Here. Take this and eat it, Mary.

Take, eat, this is the token of our kinship. If evermore apart, we are together still. Take, eat, share with one another, for surely we love each other. It will not be forever thus. Our hands will lose their grasp and our feet the common way. Yet we are forever bound, one to one, all to all, heart to heart, by love's unbreaken chain.

"Is this your bestest birthday ever, Our Mam?" I asked my mother, but she was smiling at my father, offering her cake to his lips.

Red Sails in the Sunset

The first time I saw Death I didn't recognise him. What I saw was 'Tommy Tucker' Taverner, sitting on Mrs. McNally's doorstep, hugging his knees. Tommy was one of the fixtures on the streets of Jarrow, summer and winter, a drunken old man in a jacket and trousers that didn't match and a muffler like a dead snake hanging round his neck. His face was so ingrained with sooty grime you'd think the furrows had been painted black. He was barred from the decent public houses and folks would cross the road to avoid him, but he rarely gave offence to anyone. He was mortally addicted to the red biddy, but he would drink anything that would hasten him his exit from consciousness. He would sing in the street for pennies, but he couldn't hold a note and his raucous bellowing was simple blackmail.

But Uncle Freddie explained to me that this skeletal wreck was once Sergeant Major Thomas Taverner D.S.M. M.M. who fought against the Zulus and the Boers in the name of Queen and King and Country. In the desperate days of the Great War when any warm body would do to plug the gaps in the ranks Tommy Taverner became a non-combatant private in the Army Service Corps where in March, 1918, he found himself once again up to his armpits in muck and bullets with a Lee-Enfield in his hands

Tommy rallied a handful of stragglers and held a broken German blockhouse against battalion strength until every man was dead or wounded, gaining valuable time for the stricken Fifth Army. Tommy had three body wounds and his bloody scalp hanging over his eyes so the German medico thought he was dead until the corpse reached up and tugged his trousers. Tommy became a Prisoner of Honour because whatever you may think of the Germans they respected valour. I tell you this true story lest you should forget what men of honour your great grandfathers were, but I weep for those lost generations, men and women, cheated and slaughtered by the ignorance and cupidity of politicians.

So Tommy Tucker rode for free on Uncle Freddie's tram along with legless Jimmy Hunter and others. When Tommy climbed on board Uncle Freddie would salute smartly, saying, "All present and correct, Sergeant Major!" Tommy would attempt to return the salute and Uncle Freddie would stop him falling backwards off the tram. Tommy rode on top where his stink would blow away and not bother anybody, riding all day from Jarrow down to Shields pier head and back. When I asked Uncle Freddie why he saluted him he answered, "I salute the man, not the uniform." That's how I knew who Tommy Tucker really was.

The morning I found Tommy Tucker sitting on Mrs. McNally's doorstep I said, "Good morning, Mr. Taverner," but he didn't answer or raise his head. I hadn't taken two steps before Mrs. McNally opened her front door and Tommy Tucker fell backwards into her passage. I stood transfixed.
"No, you don't, Tommy!" cried Mrs. McNally and when he didn't move, stirred the corpse with her foot, "Away with yi afore I get the pollis!"
She was a fierce woman was Mrs. McNally and wouldn't have needed any help from the constabulary. Even Chapman's dog ran away from her.
Then she realised he was dead and fell to her knees, saying, "Ah, you poor man!" and repeated, "You poor man!"
It was said with such feeling I knew he was dead, but it was the compassion that was surprising. I must've been frozen for she said to me, "Don't stand gawping, Lecky Fergie, away to Doctor Marks! Tell him he's wanted."
Then she did something else that surprised me. She didn't push Tommy out on to the pavement and shut the door. She lifted his poor corpse into her passage, onto her new linoleum. This was how Thomas Taverner came home to the house where he was born.

The Fergies were at peace with the world for once which was rare in our house. I was lying on my bed writing a letter to Shirley Temple and my mother was sewing. My father was his usual restless self, reading the paper, snorting at what he read and itching to start trouble. He opened his mouth to give my mother the benefit of what he had read and disagreed with, but she said, without looking up, "I don't want to know, Davie, thank you very much."
When it looked as if he'd persist, she said, "Yi'll just drive me into the kitchen."
He closed his mouth and looked round for someone else to persecute.

Attack being the best form of defence, I said, "How'd'y'spell "pusillanimous", Our Dad?"
He glared at me and said, "Hey! I'm reading the paper, you're writing daft pomes like a lass. Don't involve me."
My mother smiled into her sewing.
I finished my letter, bringing Shirley up to date on the exciting events that had happened recently in Jarrow: such as the scandal of Mrs. Sneap's parrot that had finally spoken, singing 'Vote, vote, vote for Winston Churchill' thus exposing itself as a rank Tory and then flew up the chimney never to be seen again.
I addressed the envelope and went through my stamp box for a stamp that hadn't been used too much. I posted all my letters with stamps where the cancellation was very faint which you could make even fainter with a judicious application of bleach or stamps where the cancellation had just caught the edge and you could tear that bit off. The next move was to slide into the kitchen where a touch of condensed milk would secure the stamp to the envelope.

As soon as I started to move slowly, cautiously, as if I was just falling off the bed I offered myself as a target to my father who pounced, asking, "What's the difference between your Uncle Freddie and a real tram conductor?"
"Oh, give it a rest, Davie," begged my mother.
Trapped between my father and the door I fought back, saying, "What's wrong with him giving the bairns a free ride down to Shields sands?" echoing my revered uncle.
"Come on! What's the difference?" persisted my father.
I appealed to my mother.
"Tell him it's not funny any more, Our Mam!"
"What's the difference?" my father repeated.
My mother said, "You heard him, Davie. It's not funny."
Quoting Uncle Freddie, I accused him, "Would you take the last penny from an old wife's purse?"
"Freddie should thank his lucky stars," my father answered, "that Tommy Taverner didn't hand in his mess tin riding upstairs on his tram."
"At least Freddie kept him out of the pub," my mother retorted.
"Come on," my father insisted, "What's the difference between Freddie and a real conductor?"
As he now had hold of my arm cutting off the blood supply to the fingers that held my precious stamp it seemed simpler to humour him.
"Five bob," I said, resignedly.
"Wrong!" he crowed with delight, "Y'wrong! Ten bob."
My mother stopped sewing and looked up anxiously.

"Freddie's working overtime," my father explained, "Dishing out free rides to the unwashed."
My mother, concerned, said, "I hope that's not true, Davie."
"Of course, it's true," said my father, "It's the talk o' Jarrow. That trams's never been so busy. Standing room only with Freddie."
"You are exaggerating, I hope," she said, forgetful of her sewing.
"For starters, he's got Jimmy Hunter stuck up front every day like a figurehead," answered my father.
My mother flared up and asked, "And why not? The lad's given enough!"
There wasn't much more Jimmy Hunter could give. On the first of July, 1916, the 4th Tyneside Scottish were massacred before La Boiselle, and Sergeant James Hunter became Wee Jimmy, losing both legs at the hip. Wee Jimmy travelled on a homemade bogie which he pushed and pulled round Jarrow with his lumpy knuckles.
"You mark my words," my father warned, "One day soon they'll catch up with him and then Freddie'll be for the high jump."
"What high jump?" I cried in panic. Was my beloved uncle to be entered for some sinister athletic event in which the true state of his underwear would be exposed? Or, worse still, was he to imitate the fearful fate of Hugh Hanstanley, the embezzling Vicar's Warden, who jumped from the vestry roof of St. Dunstan's crying, "Farewell, cruel world!" only to land on Daft Duncan's cart making crème de la pomme de terre of four sacks of King Edward's. As he lay with the breath knocked out of him, Duncan's dog welcomed him back to this cruel world, fastening his teeth into a very sensitive portion of Hanstanley's anatomy.
My telepathic mother said, "Lecky, don't start your nonsense!"
"Look," my father said, reasonably enough, "It's the way Freddie is."
"Meaning?" said my mother.
"He doesn't believe he should have the job. Not when there's real tramways men on the dole."
"It would break Bella's heart," my mother said, thoughtfully, "If he lost that job."
"I doubt it," my father said, "She's not counting on a pension."
"A weekly wage would do," said she, biting off an errant thread.
"Well," said the family cynic, "I doubt he's selling enough tickets to cover his money."
"He sells lots of tickets," I declared loyally.
"Who to?" my father asked, "Not to Jimmy and the rest of the non-ticket-buying public from Hurworth Place, he's not. Go on then! Who to?"
I defended my illustrious uncle stoutly.

"The first day when Inspector Gordon was on he even sold a ticket to a dog."
My father laughed and bent to lace his boot.
"How Jarrow & District managed before you lot started using the trams beats me."
"He's a very good conductor," I replied, "Everybody likes him."
My father stood up, his enjoyable leisure time within the family circle ending, and braced himself to head off to his work.
"I bet they like him," he said.
This robust encounter is a shadow of the bitter arguments I had with my father in later years. Neither of us would ever let go any more than Daft Duncan's dog would release Hanstanley's buttock. The pair of them were loaded onto the stretcher together.
"He always helps the old wives with their baskets," I cried and my mother joined in, saying, "Freddie's right. The disabled should ride for free."
My father rewarded my mother with the understanding smile the lunatic asylum keeper reserves for his feeble-minded charges.
"D'y'think the bosses lose any sleep over the likes of Jimmy Hunter?"
"Well, they should," responded my mother defiantly, "A land fit for heroes they said."
My father shook his head sadly at his favourite lunatic, and turned to leave the ward. He stopped at the door to say to me, "Tell yi what yi should do, Lecky," in encouraging tones.
"What?" I said cautiously.
"Get your Granny started on making two prison suits."
"What for?"
A wavelet of panic ran over me as the incoming tide slides over the shore. My father opened the door and said, "Cos you're gona need them. You and your precious uncle. Mebbes they'll let yi share a cell?"
"Get yourself away, Davie," my mother called, "Ya frightening the bairn."
"I'm going," he said, and to me, "Get her to make them with big black arrows on them."

We listened to his laughter and boots on the stairs. We heard the front door slam. And so my father marched off to work content with the harmony he had created in our happy home.
"If you're going to dip that dirty stamp in my condensed milk you'd best do it now when I'm not looking," said my mother so I went to the kitchen, dipped a finger in the condensed milk tin, transferred the glutinous mucilage to the back of my stamp, stuck the stamp most carefully and precisely on the envelope, kissed the envelope flap where Shirley's fingers would open the letter, licked my

finger clean, dipped it again in the condensed milk, sucked off the dairy delight and returned to the Room.

"Will we go to prison, Our Mam?" I asked, settling down beside her knees. She smelled, as ever, of carbolic soap and saintliness.

"What happens when the Inspector gets on?" she asked, carefully avoiding the issue of her son becoming a convict, endlessly tramping a treadmill while picking oakum.

I said, "Everybody gets off."

My mother folded up the pillow slip and reached for another.

"Doesn't he notice the rush?" she asked.

My mother was the still, calm centre of the world. Where she was there was rarely commotion and bustle. In her presence there was a certainty, a surety that dispelled fear. A working class woman she was at heart a peasant, content to accept each day, to trust herself to God's mercy.

I explained to her, "Gasser Gillespie, that's Uncle Freddie's driver, he watches up the line and gives a shout when he sees the Inspector."

"Then what?" my mother asked, threading her needle with the eyesight of a kestrel.

"He slows down and everybody jumps off."

"The old wives jump off?"

I laughed and said, "No, he stops for them. But it's easier from Tyne Dock down to the pier head at Shields."

"How's that?" she said, sewing a line of stitches as neat as any machine.

"The Shields Inspectors won't let the Jarrow Inspectors on their line."

She stopped for a moment to consider this statement and then asked, "But don't they notice what's going on?"

"The Jarrow Inspectors won't let the Shields Inspectors on their trams," I explained and my mother began to laugh.

Then she became very serious and said, "All the same it'll end in tears unless we put a stop to it."

"They won't catch us," I reassured her, but her face said she didn't believe me.

On the following Saturday just as we left the shadow of Tyne Dock Arches, turning onto the Jarrow Road, Inspector Gordon appeared from nowhere and swung aboard the old Jarrow No. 2.

"Tickets, please!" the Inspector cried, "Have your tickets ready for inspection, if you please!"

I was petrified. Inspector Gordon was a monster with a dragon's bad breath, a moustache like the burning bush and a mop of curly ginger hair like his cap was on fire. He'd been hiding in the shadow of Tyne Dock Arches, waiting to ambush us. If Uncle Freddie was to be saved from the indignity of a suit speck-

led with black arrows there was nothing forrit but for me to play the hero. I leapt down the stairs, kicked him up the backside and jumped off the tram.
"Yi little bugger!" he roared, "I'll give yi something to remember when I get aholt of you!"
I didn't wait to find out what it was he was going to give me in remembrance, but I heard the tram bell behind me and the screech of brakes. As the tram slowed the Ginger Giant jumped down after me as I ran like the wind down the Jarrow road. Never before or since have I run so fast, fuelled by the furious threats borne on the wind behind me. Certainly faster than Pheidippedes. Before I turned off across the fields for the Cemetery I heard the tram start up and move off. I felt triumphant. Whatever happened to me I didn't care. I had saved Uncle Freddie's bacon.
To make sure the Ginger Giant didn't give up and return to harass my uncle I stopped to draw breath and thumb my nose at my panting pursuer. That cheery salutation inspired him to greater efforts and he wasn't far behind me when I ran into the cemetery where Uncle Freddie and I spent many a happy hour playing hide and seek. I waited at the gate to make sure he didn't run past. Catching sight of me, he shouted angrily, "I'll give yi cemetery, y'little snot! Wait 'til I get my hands on yi!"
I didn't wait longer than to make sure he was following me. Then I burrowed among the neglected gravestones and listened to the monster prowling and raging, safe under a fallen angel.
He thrashed about for quite a time and then stood panting and raging, not ten feet from where I was hidden.
"I know where y'are!" he shouted when it was obvious that he did not.
He punished a sombre cherub with a stick and bawled, "It'll be the worse for you if I have to fetch yi out!"
Silence was the loud reply as the summer's afternoon was disturbed only by bird song.
Then he tried another tack and shouted, encouragingly, "You step out now, son, and wi'll have nowt more than a few words!"
His invitation to public debate was tempting, but my legs were shaking so much I couldn't have stood up without assistance. How the monster couldn't hear my heart beating I'll never know.
Then he lost his patience and rushed about the graveyard, shouting, "Right! You're forrit now! Yi've asked forrit! Don't try to run! I'll skin yi alive when I catch yi!" From here and there among the gravestones bewildered old men and women rose and began to run haltingly towards the gate like partridges disturbed.
His angry voice became more and more distorted, colliding with the

catafalques, tumbling over the tombstones until it was so distant that I fell into the arms of Morpheus beneath the immemorial elms. When I woke up Uncle Freddie was standing over me and the sun was sinking behind the cemetery wall.

"Oh, Uncle Freddie!" I cried, "Am I glad to see you!"

He helped me to my feet, saying, "Ditto, old son. What on earth possessed you to do that?"

"Do what?" I asked.

"Kick the Inspector up the vestibule," he replied.

We wandered together down the cemetery path towards the gate.

"Stop him inspecting the tickets," I said, "I saved your bacon."

Uncle Freddie laughed and shook his head.

"Lecky, old sausage, I don't know how to tell yi this."

I stopped and looked at his face, wrinkled with amusement.

"Tell me what?" I said guardedly.

"Gasser spotted him on the run through," my venerable uncle replied, "Everybody had tickets."

When we got home to Hurworth Place it was to find a council of war in progress. My escapade with the Ginger Giant was the last straw for my mother and Auntie Bella. They were determined that Uncle Freddie should behave himself and give up dishing out free rides.

"So, it's agreed, is it?" said my mother when the only people in agreement were the two women. Auntie Bella nodded vigorously and said, "You listening, Freddie?"

"No more free rides," my mother demanded.

"Not for anybody," Auntie Bella emphasised with an emphatic poke in the reprobate's chest, "Not even Jimmy Hunter."

"Not ever again," my mother added.

"Well?" said his wife, "Say something, Freddie."

The accused sat in the dock saying nothing, sucking on his empty pipe.

I added my two pennorth, saying, darkly, "Otherwise you're going to need a prison suit."

My mother said, "I'll sew a button on your lip in a minute."

Indignantly I replied, "I was the one nearly got murdered by the Ginger Giant!"

"How about?" said my Uncle Freddie.

"How about what?" said the two sisters in chorus.

"How about one last fandango?" my wonderful uncle replied.

"Go on," said Auntie Bella.

"How about," my Uncle Freddie declaimed, with a truly theatrical flourish, "The Hurworth Place, One'n'Only, Never-to-be-Repeated, Summer Sunday

Excursion to the Golden Sands of Shields?"

We were stunned into silence. My mother recovered most quickly and asked, "You mean steal a tram, fill it with the undeserving poor and ride it away down to the sands?"

My uncle nodded like a porcelain Mikado.

"Oh, wonderful!" I cried, "Oh, that's dapper, Uncle Freddie! Oh, let's, Our Mam! That's the best idea ever! In all the world!"

Suddenly our shabby kitchen was illumined with a wondrous light that transformed the world. As Jason and the Argonauts had set to their oars to strike the sounding furrow and row beyond the western stars so we glimpsed the awesome moment: of Jimmy Hunter re-united with his legs, of old women become young again, of old men straight and true, restored, of pale alley children sun-dazzled, of a chariot of delight travelling through a golden day to the edge of a sea bluer than Mary Pickford's eyes. We stood transfixed at the vision we shared. Should we? Would we? Could we? Dare we? The prison gates loomed large.

Auntie Bella sighed a sigh of such longing, and asked, "Wha'd'y'think, Mary? It'd be a regular lark, wouldn't it?"

My startled mother sat down on the kitchen chair and said, "Even Jesse James only robbed trains. He didn't steal them."

"We'll give it back, Our Mam," I cried, "We're only like lending it for the day."

My Uncle Freddie declared, "I know for a fact, Sunday, 22nd, Jarrow Ferret Club are away to Scarborough. And who is the head weasel?"

"Inspector Gordon!" cried Auntie Bella.

"The Ginger Giant!" I echoed.

I sought Auntie Bella's hand and she held mine tightly as we both awaited fearfully my mother's reaction.

She regarded Uncle Freddie sternly and we drew a trepidatious breath. No miserable miscreant at the Old Bailey faced a sterner King's Counsel.

"You're sure about this, are yi, Freddie?" my mother demanded.

"Abso-bally-lutely!" he affirmed, "Two years running the Inspector's won Best in Show. Wins this year he gets to keep the tin cup. He won't miss out on that."

His defending counsel joined in to ask her client a leading question, "And that would be the finish? No more free rides, Freddie? Promise?"

The prisoner in the dock raised his palm so we might see it was reasonably clean and took the oath.

"I swear," said my hero, "No more free rides. Just one last mad fling."

Overcome by the intensity of the moment, and the trembling of Auntie Bella beside me, I cried out, "Just one last mad fling, Our Mam!" To which she replied, out of force of habit, "I'll mad fling you in a minute, you daftie!"

My dear mother had this annoying habit of snatching words from my mouth

and smacking me over the head with them which was quite disconcerting.
We waited in a silence so profound we could hear next door's netty flush, the clack of the sneck and Mrs. Chamberlain emerge into the yard, singing 'You are my honey, honeysuckle, I am the bee', a song so deeply imbued with memory for me that whenever I hear it sung I cannot help but recall Mrs. Chamberlain's bumblebee form in flowered pinny and full voice emerging from their netty.
Auntie Bella said, tentatively, "Wha'd'y'think, Mary?"
My mother laughed and said, "I think it's the best we're gona get, Bella."
Auntie Bella and I hugged each other and Uncle Freddie looked suitably modest.
"Now this is what we'll do," said my hero, "Not to draw attention to ourselves."
My mother interrupted to say, "There speaks an optimist. I think I'll get Granny started on four prison suits."
But everybody laughed and Uncle Freddie went on to say, "Not to draw attention everybody walks out to the Don bridge. Anybody sees us that time of morning'll think we're going to St. Paul's."
"There's been a mass conversion overnight in Hurworth Place, has there?" suggested my mother.
"Oh, Mary, you're just nit-picking," Auntie Bella protested.
"A healthy habit," my mother said, "Go on, Freddie."
"Gasser brings up the tram from the Swinburne Street depot, but he doesn't drive on into Jarrow," explained our strategist, "He picks us up. Turns about. And we're away."
"Aye, away with the faeries," my mother said, but she laughed when Auntie Bella frowned at her.
"Once we're past Tyne Dock we're free and clear," concluded Uncle Freddie, "It's a doddle down to the pier head."
Auntie Bella said, "We still have to pass the depot, Freddie."
The eternal optimist waved away her objection.
"That time in the morning nobody'll be there, I promise yi."
He looked to us for applause.
"Another entry in the Famous Last Words Competition," sighed my mother, "Sounds like a winner to me. But I like your style, Freddie. I always have. The Hurworth Place, One'n'Only, Never-to-be-Repeated, Summer Sunday Excursion to the Golden Sands of Shields, it shall be!"

When we crept out of the front door on that famous Sunday morning, shushing each other, on tip-toe, trying not to giggle, I had never seen Albert Road so empty, so quiet. My mother and Auntie Bella carried baskets with our brawn sandwiches and bottles of liquorice water. My father, full of dark forebodings, had gone marching off to the bakery to sweep out the ovens. It was the only time the ovens were idle and my father made up his money by crawling into the unbearably hot ovens with a hand brush, yeast bags on his elbows and knees, to sweep them free of carbonised crumbs. His parting words were, "Don't forget to write and tell me what prison you're in." From this you may assume he did not approve of the Summer Sunday Excursion.

My grandfather was dressed in a suit so ancient, as my mother wittily testified, it must've been bought new for Moses's christening. My grandmother looked like Queen Victoria, only much less grumpy, with a hat slightly smaller than a bell tent.

You might have seen my grandparents without so much as saying how-de-do. They're immortalised on a penny postcard entitled The Pier, South Shields which was in McKay's window for decades growing still more shabbily sepia, ever more subtly shaded with soot. My father referred to it, with heavy sarcasm, as the Family Portrait and my grandmother, should the conversation touch upon the doings of Royalty, would sometimes say, "Mind yi, Davie and me're in McKay's window" as if this were an accolade of excellence. But she was such a sweet, loving soul I can easily forgive this slight vanity.

The postcard shows the great granite pier at South Shields and the landing stage that was used by the excursion steamer that ran upriver to Newcastle. Away in the distance is the great pier crane and the lighthouse at the end of the pier. A great host of passengers awaits the steamer. From the background a well-heeled family advances on the camera, their faces alight with interest. Look, mater, look a photographer! My word, what fun! How jolly! Heads up, children, shoulders back, chins out! Dorothy, your hat, my dear! Do attempt a smile, Julian, please!.

In the left foreground there are four ladies in wonderful hats with brims as big as cartwheels. The nearest lady is fighting to control her hat in the sharp Shields breeze. In the right foreground are my grandmother and grandfather in their Sunday best. Walking away from the camera.

When I asked Granny Fergie why they hadn't turned round so I could see their faces she said they had, but the photographer had been so abusive and threatened to turn them off the pier if they dared look at the camera again. He claimed they had wasted a valuable plate. He said he had a good mind to charge them for the unnecessary expense. At which Grandad Fergie went pale as his pockets were empty but for the tuppence he was saving to buy them both an ice cream cornet.

They had walked almost the full mile to the lighthouse before they dared peep round only to find the photographer had packed up his paraphernalia and departed.

It might have been quiet when we crept out of Hurworth Place, but in no time at all Albert Road was like a bear garden. The day trippers shouted and sang, laughed and wrestled and marched like a revolutionary army much to the amusement of casual pedestrians. The Hurworthians were out on a spree and didn't care who knew it. For Uncle Freddie to quieten them was hopeless although he managed to bring them to some sort of order and we all marched along behind him in a ragged column. It gave me a surprise to look back and see just how many there were of us. Two of the lads were hauling Jimmy Hunter along on his bogie, but even Uncle Freddie hadn't the heart to stop him playing his mouth organ. So we marched to Tipperary and Land of My Dreams.

My mother and Auntie Bella, skipping behind us, were as carefree as anyone else so it seemed to be only Uncle Freddie and I who shared anxious glances.

"D'y'know?" said my Auntie Bella, "D'y'know I cannot remember when we last had such a lark?"

She and my mother began to sing "Down to the briny where the moon's big and shiny!"

"Bella!" cried my anxious uncle, "Isn't there enough row?"

My Auntie Bella said, "Oh, come on, Freddie, you didn't really expect them to keep mum, did you?"

"No," he replied, a trifle hot under the collar, "But I didn't expect them to announce that the circus was coming to town."

My mother said, admiringly, "Freddie looks a treat. Every inch Tram Conductor of the Year."

Uncle Freddie said, "I must've been mad to start this!"

"Then let's all be mad together," cried my Auntie Bella, and chased him to kiss his embarrassed cheek which caused the whole caravan to break into a trot which might've turned into a cavalry charge if we hadn't arrived at the Causeway as the sombre bell of St. Paul's began to toll. No need to 'ask not for whom the bell tolls' on a quiet Sunday morning. It certainly catches your attention unbidden.

The whole cavalcade stumbled to a stop and everybody became quiet. We heard the rumble of the tram even before we could see it. Like an oriental juggernaut it crossed the Don Bridge and came to rest, windows winking in the sunlight. Uncle Freddie went to talk to his driver, Gasser Gillespie. The women settled in the sun like contented cats. The lasses began to make daisy chains and the lads wrestled and rolled about on the grass. The men walked about talking and kicking at the grass clumps as if they couldn't control their feet. My grandparents, like rustic, rusty sweethearts, walked towards the Don bridge to gaze upon that silver stream: silver with mercury, that is.

"What's Freddie up to?" Auntie Bella asked of the morning sunlight.

My mother shaded her eyes to look at him in close conversation with Gasser.
"Whatever it is he's taking his time," she said.
I said, "I'll just go and see what's up."
I got up to run to them, but my mother pulled me down.
"You'll just stay out of it, Socrates," said she.
The men having punished the grass clumps to their satisfaction squatted on their honkers, waiting as patiently as they always waited. At Palmer's Gate. Outside the Labour Exchange. In the trenches on a summer's day of a certain July.
Gasser got back up into the tram and Uncle Freddie came over to us.
Reading his face, Auntie Bella asked, "What is it, Freddie?"
The great man grimaced and answered, "A tiny hitch, my angel."
"A contradiction in terms," my mother retorted, "Hitches only come in one size. Goliath."
Uncle Freddie sat down on his honkers and plucked a blade of grass.
"The Ferret Club's not off yet," he reported and thumbs together blew a forlorn note from the grass reed.
"I knew, I knew when he said 'my angel'," sighed Auntie Bella, "He never offers me sugar without vinegar."
My mother, shrewdly, demanded, "Your concern for the Ferret Club is commendable, Freddie, but is there some little detail you haven't mentioned?"
"The Inspector's on sentry-go outside the depot," he confessed.
"You'll never get this lot past him," decided Auntie Bella, sadly.
"Any other good news?" my mother asked, "The Germans back in Sunderland, are they?"
This was a somewhat bitter reference to the day Granny Fergie, perusing the paper with her patched-up specs, screamed aloud causing my mother to drop and break her precious vegetable dish, crying out, "Eeh, my God, the Germans are in Sunderland!" when they had, in truth, marched into the Sudetenland.
Uncle Freddie bared his teeth and admitted, "Sorry, but we'll have to keep to the timetable."
My mother and Auntie Bella exchanged glances that can only be described as glances aghast.
"Who's gona tell this lot their outing is off?" asked my mother and Auntie Bella looked close to tears.
"Oh, Freddie!" she cried.
The tolling of the bell stopped.
"They'll hang him from the belfry rope," my mother decided with some satisfaction. Her sister began to cry.
"Will that be before or after the collection?" I wondered.

With impressive dignity Inspector Gordon withdrew his watch from the waistcoat pocket of his Sunday suit and glared at Number Two rumbling past for Shields. Unfortunately the tram was running dead on time so there was little occasion to vent on the crew his barely suppressed frustration at the unpunctuality of the motor charabanc booked to carry the Ferret Club to Scarborough. Petrol vehicles couldn't compete with the military precision of the tramways. The Ginger Giant snorted with contempt, automatically noting Motorman Gillespie at the controls and Conductor Dean on the back platform. He counted the passengers. There were only five. As expected it was a waste of time running a tram this hour of a Sunday morning. They'd pick up nobody through Tyne Dock, Low Shields and down to Shields pier head.

Inside the tram muffled groans, screams, protests, cries of pain to wring the hardest heart competed with the mechanical clatter and rattle of the vehicle. The Hurworth Place, One'n'Only, Never-to-be-Repeated, Summer Sunday Excursion to the Golden Sands of Shields was piled on the seats and floor, three deep in places, re-enacting the agonies of the Black Hole of Calcutta. Women and girls were stacked downstairs like firewood. Men and boys filled the upper deck like so many protesting sardines, groaning and cursing only mildly because it was Sunday. Five grannies in iron corsets sat upright on wheezing ribcages. Such grannies could be rolled like barrels, but not bent. To coin a phrase, every nook hid a granny.

The almost unbearable torment was unremitting until Gasser drew the tram to a halt in the shade of Tyne Dock Arches. Then the cries of relief, the groans of tortured joints, the exhalation of renewed breath echoed under the Arches like the wailing of banished banshees, the dying of a clan of bagpipes, the scraping of numberless nails down an endless blackboard as the Summer Sunday Excursion sorted itself out, glared about indignantly, adjusted bonnets, rescued clay pipes from throats, retrieved battered dignity, uncrumpled little girls, recovered babies from the ticket locker and resuscitated elderly relatives. Nobody died on the Hurworth Place Summer Sunday Excursion. But it was a damn close-run thing.

At Shields pier head under a glorious summer sun Uncle Freddie dismissed his troops with the sharp injunction that the Jarrow Special would leave the pier head at nine sharp, not a minute later, and that anyone who missed the tram would have to walk home to Jarrow. It was the most marvellous of days ever. My mother and Auntie Bella splashed in the waves just like the lasses they once had been. Grandad, with his boots on laces around his neck, and Granny under her amazing bonnet waded along the water's edge like sweethearts, hand in hand. Tommy Capstick carried Jimmy Hunter piggyback to the water's edge in his shirt-tails where he balanced on his knobby knuckles and spouted seawater when the waves knocked him over, shrugging off Tommy's helping hands as he struggled to right himself.

I said to my mother, "Y'd think he'd be frightened of drowning, wouldn't yi, Our Mam?"

My mother looked at the mutilated man, splashing and laughing at the water's edge.

"What's left to frighten Jimmy Hunter?" she said and stroked my head.

Later there were sandwiches liberally salted with sand and tea for the grown-ups made with hot water from the kiosk on the promenade that Auntie Bella said wasn't the same article as home.

On the promenade by the Brigade House there was a crew of Royal Air Force men putting up a barrage balloon.

"Why're they doing that, Our Mam?"

"T'warn the Germans off from coming over to spoil our outing with their bombs," she said and I wasn't sure she was joking.

"But that's in Spain," I explained, "They're not coming here. Are they?"

"Better safe than sorry," said my mother, "You can't be too careful."

The balloon cast an elephant's shadow as it rose, flapping, into the bright blue yonder, a darkening shadow that would change our lives forever and mark the end of my childhood. But today I was content with the beach, the silver sea and the dark-fringed pools below the pier. Across the beach the sun-bleached voices and the faerie music of the fairground drifted to where I explored another world where tropical flowers blossomed and alien claws scuttled across a rocky floor. I bent my head and slid my arm into the magic mirror.

At nine o'clock the men were missing, absent without leave. Except for Jimmy Hunter. But even with the SPECIAL board up a small dark man with a beard, pince nez, carrying an attaché case, tried to get on our tram. Uncle Freddie, standing on the platform, stopped him by stepping in front of him and politely returned him to the pavement.

"I'm sorry, sir," said Uncle Freddie, with a smile, "But yi cannot."

The man looked puzzled and said, in a foreign accent, "This is a Jarrow tram, is it not?"

"Yes, sir, it is," said my uncle, politely, "But it's a SPECIAL."

"A special?" repeated the man.

"A SPECIAL, sir," the polite conductor smiled.

The foreign gentleman considered this statement for a moment while passengers boarded the tram. Then he tried again.
"You are going to Jarrow?"
"Yes, sir," said my patient uncle, "We are going to Jarrow."
The foreign gentleman moved to board the tram and said, firmly, but politely, "I too wish to go to Jarrow."
My uncle moved to stop him, saying, "This is a SPECIAL, sir. There'll be a service tram along in ten minutes."
The foreigner allowed his exasperation to show, saying, "What is a special? I do not understand this special."
Uncle Freddie made one last effort to explain.
"SPECIAL's a board we put up when a club has hired the tram for an outing," he explained and then, seeing in the stranger's face the inevitable question forming about 'outing' he surrendered, saying, "Oh, haway, come aboard, sir, come aboard. What's one more for the Skylark?"
"This vehicle has a name?" asked the stranger.

The foreign gentleman sat next to me, but I didn't explain that this was a very special SPECIAL where nobody bought tickets, but sometimes you had to lie down and hide in very trying circumstances. He was very curious about who we were and how we lived and I told him how Uncle Freddie got his job on the trams by accident and how he felt about taking a job that he knew wasn't really his. By the time we were running through Low Shields, David Bronstein, for that was his name, knew everything about the Fergies and the Deans. It's impossible not to make friends on a tram. The eccentrically erratic movement of the vehicle brings people together as it rattles along the lines and lurches round corners like a drunken man heading for home.

Watching a relieved and relaxed Uncle Freddie moving among his happy day-trippers Mr. Bronstein said, "A man with a mind of his own. I like the sound of this Uncle Freddie."
"He's my very best friend," I said, "We suit each other right up to the sky."
"There is no greater distance for friendship to travel," replied my new friend, "Have you also a father?"
When I told him about Our Dad he said how lonely he must be sweating on the ovens all night long, leaving my mother lonely in an empty bed. I had never thought of that before.
"He sounds like a fighter to me this father of yours," suggested Mr. Bronstein, "He will not lie down and call quits for anyone, eh?"
"He gets very angry," I apologised, "Our Mam says it's his leg."

The stranger nodded sagely, and replied, "I have known men like that. He must be very proud of you, Sasha?"
Sasha is a pet name in Russian for Alexander.
I shook my head.
"I don't think so."
Mr. Bronstein appeared puzzled.
"Why do you say that?" he asked, "You are his son."
"I can't do anything right for him," I said sadly.
"Do you talk to him? Not about the weather. About important things that a father and son should discuss. "
"No. He never talks to me," I answered.
"Like many fathers," said David Bronstein, "Perhaps he does not know how. You must teach him, Sasha."
"Me?" I cried, astonished, "I'm no use to anybody."
"Perhaps your father fears that of himself," he suggested enigmatically and as Uncle Freddie approached, "Ah! Forgive me! I have forgotten to purchase a ticket."
He caught Uncle Freddie by the tunic as he passed and said, "Excuse me, Mr. Conductor Uncle Freddie!"
"Yes, sir?" said my expansive uncle, basking in the approbation of his happy passengers, "How can I help you?"
David Bronstein dug into his pocket and produced a purse.
"I have been most remiss," he apologised, "I have not purchased a ticket from you."
Uncle Freddie said, "You've no need of a ticket, sir," and made to pass on.
"But I must purchase a ticket like everyone else," said David Bronstein, "Then we are all special together."
Uncle Freddie was going to argue, but then recognised the same steely determination in the voice that had persisted until allowed aboard the SPECIAL and relented. David Bronstein, I had already learned, was a relentless debater.
"If you wish to buy a ticket, sir," my uncle agreed, "Then who am I to stop you throwing your money about? That will be tuppence, sir, in English money."

Jimmy Hunter was playing his mouth organ and at the end of that happiest of days the trippers were all singing 'Red Sails in the Sunset'. It was a song that always made me feel sad. As if something beautiful was ending. Childhood, perhaps? Innocence? Uncle Freddie said it filled the bill in that summer twilight.
'Red sails in the sunset,' sang the women and the girls, 'Way out on the sea, Oh, carry my loved one home safely to me.'
David Bronstein asked, "What is this 'red sails'?"

"Oh, it's just a song," I said, "Everybody sings it. You can hear it on the wireless."

But it was more than a song. It was more than the scent and flavour of the fading summer evening. It was a song that filled the hearts of ordinary men and women with an inarticulate longing for lost places never seen and lost loves whom they had never embraced. It breaks my heart still to hear that old song. I remember one evening standing on the pier with my mother watching the fleet of herring drifters with their red sails set leaving the Tyne at sunset and being overwhelmed with such emotion as brought me to tears. When my mother had dried my eyes I asked her, "Why do we cry when we see something beautiful?" "Because it doesn't last, bonny lad," she said, and I knew she'd been affected by the leaving of the drifters.

David Bronstein laughed and said, "Just a song? But such a song! They sing very well Red Sails in the Sunset."

At first I had suspected that he was a secret spy sent out by Jarrow Tramways to catch Uncle Freddie, but I soon realised he wasn't. David Bronstein told me he had been living in Turkey and that he was going to America where he had friends.

"The greatest thing in life," David Bronstein told me, "To have true friends."

"But isn't money important?"

He laughed and said, "Of course! Anyone who told you otherwise would be a fool! But you won't starve if you have true friends."

"But what if they have no money?"

He laughed louder and because he was laughing the passengers around laughed too, all in good humour.

"Then you starve in good company," he asserted.

"I have a true friend," I said, "My Uncle Freddie."

"Yes," he said, "To gain friendship one must love and you do. I can see you love this man."

This was very embarrassing because 'love' was not a word we used in Jarrow.

"Does it show?" I cried in some distress and he laughed and pressed my hand, telling me what I already knew, that Alexander was a very famous name. How Alexander had set out to conquer the world.

"But in the end," said David Bronstein, "there were no more worlds to conquer. Now this was bad enough for it was his business conquering worlds and putting everything to rights. But what was worse, far worse, Alexander did not have a true friend in all the worlds."

"Not one?" I cried, horrified.

He shook his head, sadly, knowingly. Under the dark carapace of Tyne Dock Arches his voice echoed, "Not one in all the worlds he had conquered. There were thousands who were afraid of him. Hundreds of thousands who would bow and scrape to him. There were even those who would worship him as a god. But not one true friend on whom he could trust."

The words echoed and repeated.

"How awful!" I said and I knew without knowing that my new friend was talking of something other than an ancient hero.

The tram ran through the Arches and turned on to the Jarrow road.

"Prize friendship above all else, Sasha," he advised, "Even above the love of women."

I guessed he had been let down by friends who only pretended to friendship. He smiled often, but he was a very sad man.

"Alexander," said David Bronstein, "Do you know what the name means?"

"A leader of men," I said, "I've got the wrong name."

"Why do you say that?"

"I'm not a leader of anything," I admitted, "I'm a coward."

David Bronstein laughed.

"Until you need to be brave, Sasha. You will see. I was much the same myself. Until I found what I would fight for. Then I was called the Lion."

Even to a child it was apparent that there was something leonine about the man although much diminished, but an iciness of purpose, a steeliness of will remained that would be difficult to defeat.

It had been the happiest of days. It was the loveliest of evenings. We were coming towards the Don Bridge where we had started from when the tram started to slow down. Then everything went horribly wrong.

Gasser swung open his door and shouted down the saloon, "It's the Inspector, Freddie! Waving us down!"

The tram began to slow to a stop. The singing faltered and failed. An awful silence fell as the tram came to a halt. Then someone began banging on the side of the tram.

"Off!" shouted a familiar voice, "Off this tram everybody who don't have a valid ticket issued under the regulations of the Jarrow & District Electric Traction Company. Which I have in my hand should any person wish to consult the regulations!"

"What's going on, Freddie?" Auntie Bella asked unnecessarily as the mutter of uneasy voices rose like the dough in Granny's bread tins proving in her fender.

"Oh, crikey moses!" I cried, "It's the Ginger Giant!"

"It's Nemesis, Bella," said my mother resignedly, "Catching up on us as we should've known he would."

"I'm sorry, my angel," said my uncle, sadly humbled, "We've been rumbled."

"What an end to a perfect day," said Auntie Bella.
"Still we did have the day," I reminded her.
The chorus of bewildered voices rose to a crescendo and Uncle Freddie called out, "Everybody stay where you are until we sort this out, thank you!"
Inspector Gordon was not alone and it was with apprehensive eyes that we looked out on the gang of unpleasant men surrounding the tram. The Inspector mounted to the platform.
"Off! Everybody who cannot show a valid ticket dismount now and give your name and address to my colleague!" he cried, "When you have given your name and address you will be free to leave."
"Look," said Uncle Freddie, "It's just women and children. They're all tired. Why don't you let them finish their journey into Jarrow? What odds does it make?"
The Inspector ignored his plea and demanded, "Ticket board, Dean," and shouted down the saloon, "Stay where you are, Gillespie! I'll deal with you later."
Uncle Freddie submitted, "Gasser had nothing to do with this little lark."
"Oh, it's a lark, is it?" replied the Inspector, riffling through Uncle Freddie's ticket board, "Defrauding the Company, I'd call it."
He looked at the bewildered passengers and said, "Are you deaf? Everybody who hasn't got a ticket, get off this tram! Now!"
The Hurworth Place, One'n'Only, Never-to-be-Repeated, Summer Sunday Excursion to the Golden Sands of Shields began reluctantly to climb down from the tram to be imprisoned in a rough circle by the menacing accomplices of Inspector Gordon whose colleague began to collect names and addresses in a notebook. In a moment of bravado I cried out, "Never give your right name!"
My mother yanked me from the platform so fast I almost left a hand clinging to the post.
"Are you out of your mind?" she cried.
"W.C. Fields said not to," I explained.
"I'll double you see fields you in a minute !" she cried, true to form.
When everybody had shuffled off the tram and stood penned like cattle between the thugs, David Bronstein appeared on the platform to ask, "Excuse me, please. What is going on here?"
The Inspector turned to see this slight figure holding his attaché case, and shouted, "Oi, you! Off! Or do you want to be fetched off?"
"This is not Jarrow?" asked the foreign gentleman.
"No," said the Ginger Giant, "But you're not going to Jarrow. This is as far as you go."
David Bronstein said, "But I insist. I wish to go to Jarrow."
The Inspector laughed. It was an unpleasant sound and echoed by his thugs.

"Oh, you insist, do yi?" he said, and turning to his thugs, "Billie, help the gentleman off the tram."
Billie approached the step and reached up to take Mr. Bronstein's arm, but hesitated and then withdrew his arm when the foreign gentleman said, in a voice of steel, "Do not lay a hand on me. Or you will regret it."
A subdued Billie turned his flattened nose and cauliflower ear towards his employer who stepped forward to threaten, "If you don't get down you'll be fetched down. And I promise you'll regret it."
He nodded at Billie, but David Bronstein said, "But I have purchased a ticket."
The Inspector, surprised, said, "Yi have? Now that's a surprise."
David Bronstein called to Uncle Freddie, "What is happening, Uncle Freddie? Is this part of the jolly fun of the SPECIAL?"
"Let me see your ticket," said the Inspector and the ticket was passed down to him.
"I'm sorry, Mr. Bronstein," called Uncle Freddie, "But I did try to stop you getting on the tram."
The Inspector checked the ticket and grudgingly returned it to the passenger.
"I'm sorry to have incommoded you, sir, but you will be taken to your destination with as little delay as possible as you are a bona fide passenger. Please accept my apologies for any inconvenience caused."
David Bronstein shook his head, saying, "I do not understand what you are saying."
"God save me from foreigners!" cried the Ginger Giant.
"What has Uncle Freddie done that you behave in this way? Herding these good people off the tram! What are you? Are you police?" David Bronstein demanded.
The Inspector turned to make faces to his accomplices who laughed and then addressed the peculiar foreign gentleman.
"Although it is none of your business, sir, I will tell you that this man here, F. Dean, has been permitting the public to ride on the tram without buying a ticket thereby defrauding the Company of considerable revenue."
"All these people?" cried David Bronstein incredulously.
"Now you've got it!"
David Bronstein said, "I am the only one with a ticket?"
"The only one, sir."
David Bronstein cried, "How wonderful!" and began to laugh, but checked himself when the odious Inspector said, referring to Jimmy Hunter on his bogie, "And I am reliably informed that he has permitted this cripple here to travel at the expense of the Company whenever he pleases."
There was an angry murmur from the crowd like a dog disturbed.

"And that is a crime?" said David Bronstein in a voice of ice.
"Indeed it is, sir," said the Inspector, "A very serious matter as you will understand."
"Oh, I do understand," cried David Bronstein, in a voice that sent shivers up my spine, "Thank God there are still men living and breathing who understand the meaning of comradeship! He gave a free seat to un mutilé de guerre! A wounded soldier! That is a crime? Shame on you that you do not permit such brave men to ride freely whenever they wish!"
There was a tide beginning to sweep through the crowd of women, a wave of anger gathering before breaking.
"And a free ride to the sea-and-side for these poor women and children of Hurworth Place!" continued the impassioned orator, "That is a crime? God bless Uncle Freddie! The greater crime, you miserable creature, is to shut them out of the sunlight! Bravo for uncle Freddie, I say again!"
There were voices now in the crowd, angry voices where before there had been passive submission. Now there was rebellion brewing.
"Bravo for Uncle Freddie!" I cried, "Isn't it exciting, Our Mam?"
"Remember those prison suits," she said, but she was gripping my hand tightly and her eyes were bright, "Your Granny's got enough to do without you making extra work for her."
"Well, thank you very much for your opinion, sir," said the Inspector in a very strained voice, "I'm sure that where you come from you do things differently," and raising his voice, he called out to the driver, "Gillespie! Take this gentleman through to Jarrow!"
"In my country," said David Bronstein in a voice that pinned the Tramways Inspector to the spot, " In my country we would shoot cowardly hyenas and these pigs with you, on your knees in the street. And you would beg forgiveness before the bullet! That's what we would do with scum like you!"
The roar of the crowd was exhilarating. The thugs were floundering, faced with the angry women. The fuse was burning, racing towards the gunpowder.
The Inspector turned away from the tram, saying, "That's enough. Get him down from that tram, Billie."
The ensuing explosion was comparable with the awesome landmines that sent the Messines ridge skyward. There is no power on earth comparable to tired women in a fury.
The amazons, grannies and all, launched themselves at the astonished thugs, punching, spitting, biting, grabbing hair and testicles. I was shocked at my mother and Auntie Bella's behaviour as they leapt like wild cats upon the biggest bully. In the same instant as Uncle Freddie punched Billie's bulging belly button as the lout tried to pull David Bronstein from the platform, Jimmy

Hunter launched forward his bogie and cracked the Ginger Giant in the shins, bringing him down to his own level where Jimmy secured him in a crushing half-nelson in no time. As Billie bent down reflexively to inspect the damage to his particulars he was just in time to wipe his nose on Uncle Freddie's fist and lost further interest in the proceedings. When Billie fell off the tram like a dead elephant the thugs decided the game was up and ran away leaving three of their chums on the ground being bounced upon by such heavyweights as Mrs. Chamberlain and Dirty Doris from the bottling plant, to the tune of 'My brother Joe was sitting on the po', an echo of some schoolyard rhyme. Only when they begged mercy for their cracked ribs were they released and ran away under a fusillade of jeers from the triumphant women and cheers from the lads and lasses.

Jimmy Hunter was sitting on Inspector Gordon's back forcing his face ever deeper into the mud until Uncle Freddie gently relaxed his murderous grip to allow the man to breathe.

David Bronstein, from the platform, cried out, "Oh, well done! Oh, jolly well done, my friends!"

This evoked cheers and applause from the Hurworth women.

"That is the way to treat such lickspittle Cossacks!" he cried, "Off with his head!"

There was a momentary pause for reflection as no one had come suitably equipped for a decapitation, but Auntie Bella, in a moment of wild inspiration, cried, "Off with his trousers!"

She bent immediately to the task surrounded by willing, laughing helpers and David Bronstein laughed loudest.

"Better still!" he cried, "An assault on dignity!"

"Pull his linings off an' all!" I cried, quite carried away by revolutionary fervour.

"Lecky!" cried my mother, who was undoing the Inspector's braces, "A little decency, please!"

David Bronstein clapped his hands with delight, and shouted," Of course, that is the English way! The decency! To off with their trousers and expose the truth! But not the linings to expose the soul! Enough and no more! That is the English way!"

"Hang the expense!" cried my Auntie Bella, "We'll have his linings! Come on, lasses!"

The women, laughing and cheering, piled in, lifting Jimmy Hunter clear, kissing him in gratitude, and pulled away the Ginger Giant's back-vented drawers, exposing flaccid buttocks and minimal manhood. To shrieks and whoops a muddy Inspector Gordon clambered to his feet caught within a cordon of wild women, struggling vainly to protect his modesty. He looked totally bewildered and I suspect, near to tears. It was difficult not to feel sorry for him, but I succeeded. The women looked to David Bronstein who cried, "What shall we do with this miserable hyena? Shall we hang him from the nearest lamp post?"

"Yes!" I cried, "hang him!"

"You are kidding, I hope?" my mother asked.

"Madam," said David Bronstein, "a simple hanging solves most problems."

"Hang him, hang him!" cried the women while the Inspector whimpered and begged for mercy.

"Don't hang him!" cried my mother, "Throw him in the Don!"

To my mother's great relief there was voluble agreement to this proposition and a miserable, protesting Ginger Giant was dragged to the bridge and, to the accompaniment of cheers and merriment, was thrown headfirst into the cloacal filth of low tide. He landed on his nose in the stinking putrefaction that was once Bede's sweet river. He sat up gasping and retching to a chorus of jeers and laughter, all petty dignity dissipated. There he was left to extricate himself.

David Bronstein said to me, "What did the good lady, your Auntie Bella, call this malodorous sewer? The Don?"

"Yes, it's the Don all right," I assured him.

Shaking his head, he said, sadly, "Thank God I am not a religious man. Or I would be looking for omens."

"You wouldn't find any omens in the Don," I told him, "There's nothing can live in there. Not even germs."

"And now you, my friend!" said David Bronstein to my Uncle Freddie.

"Who me?" cried that ebullient hero.

"Yes, you, Uncle Freddie!" insisted David Bronstein, "Throw off the uniform of bondage! Strike off your chains!"

Uncle Freddie considered this startling proposition for a moment while we all stood waiting for his response.

"You're right and no mistake," Uncle Freddie decided and threw his cap into the tram doorway.

"What're you doing?" I cried.

"Setting myself free, old sausage," my hero responded.

His jacket followed the cap to the cheers of the Hurworthians. Auntie Bella was dismayed.

"Freddie, are you out of your mind?"

"Come to me senses more like," answered our noble savage. "I'm finished with it."

"No, no!" David Bronstein urged, "You too, the trousers!"

Even Freddie baulked at disrobing his lower members.

"You're not serious?"

David Bronstein took him by the shoulder and looked him sternly in the eye.
"They are the trousers of a Cossack hyena," advised our revolutionary leader, "Off with them! Be done with it all!"
I found myself cheering with the very women who had taken to the grim task of removing men's trousers very readily. Uncle Freddie backed away warily.
"I can manage very well by myself, thank you," he said and they cheered. They would've cheered if anybody had mentioned Bisto. They were in a rare mood for cheering. It was a wonderful summer excursion with the most astonishing entertainment at no extra charge.
Auntie Bella went pink with embarrassment.
"Freddie Dean," she cried, "Don't you dare show me up!"
But she wasn't taking off her trousers, was she? Yet I was very surprised when my mother cried out, "Who started this, Bella? Go on, Freddie! Let's see your legs!"
It was all hardly behaviour that would've been applauded at the Primitive Methodists' Sunday School Outing.
"Our Mary!" Auntie Bella cried, scandalised, open wide eyes, "I'm surprised at you! Freddie Dean! Don't you dare!"
But despite his wife's admonitions Uncle Freddie climbed out of his uniform trousers and the setting sun gleamed upon his sturdy white legs below his shirt tails. Almost everyone pretended not to look at his bare backside, but almost everyone failed dismally.
"There!" Uncle Freddie said, heaving a great sigh, "I'm done with it!"
He threw the trousers onto the platform and as if that were an arranged signal, Gasser trod on his bell and reversed the tram towards the depot. As the tram passed we all saluted and waved as if the British fleet were on review at Spithead and Gasser played Reveille on his foot bell.
"Well," my Auntie Bella remarked, "if you think I'm walking back to Jarrow with you in that state you've another think coming, Freddie Dean!"
"Don't fuss so, Bella," my mother chided her, "It's all in good fun. All part of The Hurworth Place, One'n'Only, Never-to-be-Repeated, Summer Sunday Excursion to the Golden Sands of Shields!"
She raked in her bag and brought out the calico table cloth we'd used for our picnic.
"Here you are, Freddie," she said, "It'll make a bonny kilt."
To everybody's amusement and admiration Uncle Freddie improvised a kilt from the table cloth and atrocious imitations of bagpipe music rent the air.
"So! It is done!" David Bronstein declared, "Then what shall we call this regiment of the people?"
"How'd'y'mean?" I asked.

"Eureka! I have it! You are the Hurworth Place Hussars and I, the Lion, shall be your Comrade Colonel, if you wish?"
He paused and all the women who were much taken with this proud, brave, astonishing little man, cried with one voice, "We wish!"
"Good! Then I will lead you on to pull down the petty tyranny that darkens your lives."

We all cheered like bingo although we may not have been altogether clear about what we were cheering, but it was one of those rare evenings when anything and everything is possible. So we marched along the Causeway and up Church Bank, the Hurworth Place Hussars with Uncle Freddie in his kilt, Mrs. Chamberlain flourishing the Ginger Giant's trousers, the Lion as our Colonel and Jimmy Hunter, the undefeated champion of adversity. Was there ever such another day as this? Ever such another evening in all the history of the world?
As we marched David Bronstein talked with Uncle Freddie of revolution as I hop-skipped to keep up with them.
"We must take over the Town Hall and the Police Station," insisted David Bronstein, "That is essential."
"There'll only be the cat at the Town Hall," said Uncle Freddie.
"The police station'll be shut," I put in, "They'll all be away down to the sea-side to cool their feet."
"It is also imperative," our revolutionary comrade proceeded, " that we seize the railway station and tear up the track."
"But the Baptists have gone to Jesmond for the Chapel Outing, Mr. Bronstein, "I explained, "How will they get home?"
"In a revolution the innocent are the first to suffer," David Bronstein admitted.
Uncle Freddie stopped and the whole column cannoned into one another.
"Mr. Bronstein, I can see yi mean well," said Uncle Freddie.
"Revolution is what I mean well, Uncle Freddie!"
Uncle Freddie began to march again and everybody picked themselves up and stopped asking, what went wrong then? Treading delicately so as not to offend our new friend, my Uncle Freddie explained, "I think yi'll find these lasses want to get the bairns home to bed, brew a cuppertea and put their feet up. I don't think they'll have the energy to seize the police station for you, Mr. Bronstein."
I added, "The Mams'll probably hang you from a lamp post if you stop the Baptists Outing getting back."
"But these are poor people!" insisted David Bronstein, "Robbed of employment. Barely existing in poverty. Ground under the heel of capitalism. Half-starved to keep their children fed. Children who will be the cannon-fodder of the next war. They have every cause for anger."

Uncle Freddie stopped again, but this time the column was more prepared and it was only the dozy dozen at the back who cannoned into their neighbours.
"That's where you're wrong, old son," Uncle Freddie advised, "Today they're happy. The sun is shining. They've been to the sands with the bairns and they've had a bit of a lark. Their man'll be home soon after walking off his glass of ale. And there'll be a kiss'n'a'cuddle."
David Bronstein looked at Uncle Freddie and shook his head.
"That is all they desire of life?"
"That's all they want," my uncle assured him, "Not much to ask, is it? The bairns abed, a nose red with sunburn and an hour off afore the man gets in. Come back when it's raining, Mr. Bronstein, and the washing's all in a heap and the babby's crying."
My uncle smiled at his new friend, clapped his shoulder and we marched on towards canny auld Jarrow with the Hurworth Place Hussars walking behind us, singing that heart-breaking lament, Red Sails in the Sunset, Far out on the sea, Oh, bring back my loved one, Home safely to me.

Well, that's how red revolution didn't break out in Jarrow. Pity, eh? Better a revolution than marching down to London and asking politely when the only answer is a raspberry. Reluctantly Mr. Bronstein agreed that perhaps Uncle Freddie was right, and that they weren't ready for revolution, but he insisted before we dispersed on giving a speech to the Hussars.
Auntie Bella brought out a kitchen chair and the little man climbed up to address the sunburned noses and tired children. Yet what he said held them riveted to the pavement.
"Women of Hurworth Place, I salute you!" he cried, "When I meet with my friends again I will tell them about you. I will tell them I have seen you overthrow spineless tyranny. That all is not lost when such spirit is abroad. Together you and I could change the world, rekindle the torch of freedom! Then I will tell them that before all else you put your children and your men. I salute your wisdom as I salute your courage."

Then he said the words that raised the hackles on my neck and sent a shiver up my spine. In a voice that held the Hurworth Hussars, bairns and all, motionless and unmoving, despite their tired legs, he cried out, "Comrades! And I call you comrades from the top of my heart! Let no one mislead you. I tell you the enduring verities of sacrifice and endeavour are still the eternal truths and cannot be dislodged. Despite the fists and boots of bullies they will remain as a rock when all else has turned to dust and ashes. I promise you it is so. For I have seen it here today. Thank you for your example."

That is what David Bronstein said to Jimmy Hunter, the women of Hurworth Place, Uncle Freddie and me. Wasn't that a wonderful thing to say? Sacrifice and endeavour are still the eternal truths and if there is something my poor, battered little town of Jarrow knows about it is blood, sweat and tears. On the pavement outside Hurworth Place we stood in the presence of greatness there and the women and even the children knew so too.

Auntie Bella took Mr. Bronstein in for the night. How much sleep he actually got nobody knows as he and Uncle Freddie talked half the night away. Auntie Bella chided him for not letting the visitor get his rest. David Bronstein said he'd soon have all the rest he never wanted.

The next morning I was in trouble with my mother as I tried to escape with my breakfast downstairs to talk with the exciting visitor. I was on the landing when my mother caught me and asked, "Where'd you think you're going with that?"

"Downstairs," I admitted.

"Isn't it good enough to eat your bread and dripping here then?"

"I was just taking a piece for Mr. Bronstein."

"You could eat yours first," she countered.

I fidgeted on the landing.

"I'm in a hurry, Our Mam."

In a moment of weakness she said to me, "Y'could keep me company."

I was astonished. I had no response to give.

"Go on with yi," she said.

On the stairs I said, "I'll keep you company tomorrow, Our Mam."

"Piecrust promises," she said, and then, "Lecky?"

"Yes?"

"One day," she said, "You're going to have to answer a certain question."

"What?"

She stood at the top of the stairs looking down at me, a world away, and asked me, "D'you or d'y'not, live here?"

She knew that my going away had begun just as Mr. Bronstein knew his long and painful journey was coming to its end.

"I'm your son," I said, "Course I live here."

"Just because you're my son doesn't mean y'live here," she said.

"Yes, it does, " I defended myself, "I'm only going -"

"I know where you're going," she interrupted.

She stood a million miles from me as I fiddled with the bread and dripping. Why couldn't I say she would be in my heart forever? Why couldn't I shoot up the stairs and give her a hug and a kiss? The dripping was sliding between my fingers like departing snails.

I said, "Can I go now?"

"Give Mr. Bronstein the top bread," she said, "Not the piece with your dirty fingers in."

Mr. Bronstein was lying on a shakedown in front of Auntie Bella's fire, reading a book. He sat up and closed the book when I came in. I handed him the better slice of bread and dripping.

"Breakfast in bed?" he said, "What a life of luxury I lead! You will find your admirable Auntie in the yard."

"It's Monday," I answered, "She's starting the copper fire for the wash."

Chewing his titbit, he said, "Your Uncle Freddie has gone on a mission of mercy."

"He's never been very religious before," I questioned.

David Bronstein laughed and swallowed his mouthful with difficulty.

"To find me a ship," he said, "It is time I was gone from this country."

I was disappointed.

"No, it's not!" I replied.

"That is a fine compliment to receive. On a Monday morning too. But I must be on my way."

I wanted time to talk to this exotic stranger, to learn more about him and the lands through which he had travelled.

"But where will you go, Mr. Bronstein?"

He smiled sadly, finished his bread and said, "Where is sanctuary? Tell me and I will go there immediately."

I started to rise, saying, "I could get my atlas. We could look it up," but he stopped me.

"When you are tender in years Sanctuary is easy to find. The print shrinks as one's eyes grow older."

Later that morning my Uncle Freddie took David Bronstein down to Tyne Dock where the S.S. EDUARDO SOLARON was loading coal for Panama. Uncle Freddie wouldn't take money from him, but David Bronstein cleared his pockets to Auntie Bella because he said he didn't need English money any more and he felt my Auntie could make good use of it. We didn't tell Uncle Freddie in case he swam after the ship to return the money.

And so David Bronstein left us to make his way to Mexico. To find true friends. He and Uncle Freddie exchanged letters until one dreadful day in 1940 when we heard that poor Mr. Bronstein had been murdered with an ice pick. We just couldn't believe it at first. But it was sadly true. Uncle Freddie was stunned and silent for days and I wept into my pillow for both of them. David Bronstein's real name as you have already guessed was Leon Trotsky. So, you see, Mr. Ogpu killed the lion after all.

But when I wept for this man who passed through my life on the greatest day of all days, on that halcyon summer day of The Hurworth Place, One'n'Only, Never-to-be-Repeated, Summer Sunday Excursion to the Golden Sands of Shields, I also remembered what he said to us as we stood, sunburned and weary on the hot pavement, a tiny figure standing on a kitchen chair, this giant of a man who had withstood the Great Tyrant as the women of Hurworth Place had risen against the petty tyrant.

"Let no one mislead you. I tell you the enduring verities of sacrifice and endeavour are still the eternal truths and cannot be dislodged. Despite the fists and boots of bullies they will remain as a rock when all else has turned to dust and ashes. I promise you it is so."

And it is so.